THE LIBRARY OF LITERATURE

Under the General Editorship of
John Henry Raleigh & Ian Watt

FIVE MIDDLE ENGLISH NARRATIVES

The Library of Literature

FIVE MIDDLE ENGLISH NARRATIVES

Sir Orfeo

The Cursed Dancers of Colbek

Apollonius of Tyre

Floris and Blancheflour

Ywayn and Gawayn

FIVE
MIDDLE ENGLISH
NARRATIVES

EDITED WITH AN INTRODUCTION BY

ROBERT D. STEVICK

University of Washington

THE BOBBS - MERRILL COMPANY, INC.
A Subsidiary of Howard W. Sams & Co., Inc.
INDIANAPOLIS · NEW YORK

Preface

The purpose and editorial procedure of this book are explained in the Introduction. They are similar to those of *One Hundred Middle English Lyrics* (published earlier in the Library of Literature), as are also the acknowledgements. To the editors, grammarians, lexicographers, and teachers whose publications and efforts have been drawn upon in preparing this volume, I owe the measure of gratitude understood only by those who have edited centuries-old literary texts. My wife has given encouragement and ever welcome assistance in proofreading.

R. D.S.

Contents

Introduction

1. SOME SPECIAL CHARACTERISTICS OF MEDIEVAL STORIES

Stories to read and hear again—there is perhaps no better way to describe narratives in Middle English, both in regard to their historical development and their intrinsic characteristics. All five narratives in this collection are, in fact, retellings in another, special sense as well: each was translated into English from another language. *Apollonius of Tyre,* besides having been skillfully translated into English prose in the eleventh century, was continuously available from that time until (and after) Gower retold the story in English verse in the late fourteenth century. *The Cursed Dancers of Colbek* appears in an early fourteenth-century translation of a contemporary treatise, in French, on sins; the treatise contains stories to illustrate each of the sins described. *Sir Orfeo* seems to be a close imitation in English of an Anglo-Norman or Old French *lai. Ywayn and Gawayn* is an English version of Chrétien de Troyes' *Yvain,* one of the major early Arthurian romances. *Floris and Blancheflour* was apparently first translated from French into English in the mid-thirteenth century, and was already popular in other European languages. The displacement in the fourteenth century of French by English as the principal literary language in England had much to do with the appearance of these narratives in English and, it should be added, with the nature and quality of the English versions. That a number of English versions of some stories began to appear even before the fourteenth century, however, makes clear that the entertainment value of many of the narratives was prized at least as much as their literary qualities—and quite probably more.

These stories to be read and heard again characteristically differ from typical modern fictional narrative. The Middle English tales were old, familiar, and hence nearly unchangeable; the texts represent retellings far more than new literary compositions. Although it is difficult, and often of limited value, to distinguish the tale from its telling in a modern piece of fiction, it is relatively easy and often interesting to do so in the instance of an often-told, persistently popular narrative. And in the stories that follow we have several such opportunities. The story of Apollonius—concerning the incest of Antiochus and the adventures of Apollonius in shipwreck, marriage, search, and vengeance—was a good one, if somewhat loosely constructed, before Gower told it; the framework was later sufficient for Shakespeare's *Pericles*; and indeed *Apollonius of Tyre* remains a fairly good story. Gower's telling of it is competent and workmanlike, though it lacks the narrative artfulness that we may wish for. (Some of its pedestrian aspects are pointed out in the section of the Introduction dealing specifically with this narrative.) The legend of Orpheus and Eurydice also provides a good story, one that was widely known in the Middle Ages through Ovid's *Metamorphoses* and Virgil's *Georgics*. The reshaping that the legend had undergone by the time it appeared in the Middle English version of *Sir Orfeo*, however, produced another story, distinct from, though still related to, the classical account in obvious ways; the Middle English version is a less effective story, all things considered. Something of the force and significance and appeal of the old tale is clearly lost when the conclusion of *Sir Orfeo* brings the happy reunion of Orfeo and Heurodis, their successful return from an other-world, and the proving of the steward's faithfulness. But the form—the criterion now held in high esteem —is commendable; and in its actual telling *Sir Orfeo* is a very ·good narrative, probably the best of the faery romances that have survived.

The distinction between the tale and the telling of the tale can be made again in relation to *Floris and Blancheflour* and *The Cursed Dancers of Colbek*. That the tale of Floris was extremely popular (throughout Europe) suggests some intrinsic merit—the same appealing qualities of ingenious plot and guileless invention present, for instance, in tales of *The Thousand and One Nights*. The overruling passion of love that sends a young man on a single-minded and often foolhardy pursuit of his beloved *can* underlie a successful story if, at the least, the incidents are in good order and other aspects of the narrative are properly handled. The English version(s) of *Floris and Blancheflour* kept the story intact, with only minor deviations, but failed to control some aspects of the narrative and ignored others altogether. Beside *Floris and Blancheflour*, the incident on which *The Cursed Dancers of Colbek* is based may seem too slight to sustain a narrative: it is hardly more promising than the anecdotal form of the fable of the boy who cried, "Wolf!" Nevertheless, the narrative version given here, slender as it is and framed by a moral, is more successful than the narrative of *Floris*.

Ywayn and Gawayn is instructive in respect to medieval English storytelling in quite another way, for it is a good narrative based on another good narrative, but differing from its original in elements of the telling, though not in plot structure. The translator-adapter began his English version at the same point as Chrétien de Troyes' romance and followed the story line to the end. He changed the French narrative principally by dropping certain details and segments of dialogue and description: the omission of "psychologizing," irony, suspense, allusion, and description of emotion transformed the French narrative of chivalric romance into an English one of action, adventure, and marvel.

The often told story characteristically differs from typical modern fiction in other ways. One has to do with the means employed to arouse and resolve expectations. If a piece of fiction is artful, it will have at least a pattern of expectations that is interesting in itself, giving the impression of a beginning, middle, and end of a set of actions (or perhaps issues and concepts). From this truism concerning literary narrative we cannot, however, predict the materials of a narrative or the pattern into which those materials will be deployed. It is easy, as well, to forget the variety of ways in which an artful narrative can be made. In modern fiction, for the most part, we expect that the teller will invent (or at least seem to invent, with the same effect) most of his materials: originality is highly prized. It is quite otherwise with narratives whose setting, action, and many details are known as soon as the subject or the hero's name is mentioned: these narratives are not constructed to appeal to an audience by informing the hearers or readers of places, times, peoples, and events about which they have no prior knowledge. Again, a common mode of developing a short story or novel depends on the relatively modern concept of character, of personality. The unfolding of the action may be a drama of the interaction between character and circumstance (including other characters); how someone is changed by his experiences often holds our deepest interest. Character is a concept we find difficult to suppress. In most Middle English narratives, on the other hand, our concept of character is irrelevant, not to say obtrusive or anomalous. With Chaucer's Criseyde we should make an exception, with the Wife of Bath we certainly must, but with most persons, even in Chaucer's works, we should not. Even when a "character" (we inevitably use the term) in most of these older narratives thinks or talks to himself, it is more to inform us of his strategy of action than to interest us in his psyche. Delineation of character or progressive character development and change are foreign to most narratives in fourteenth-century England, and the narrative must be made with other materials. Those materials are fundamentally action and description.

This is not to say that action and description exist merely for their own sake, though they sometimes apparently do: the narrative may also have some larger meaning or purpose. This meaning may be overtly declared: thus the ostensible purpose of *The Cursed Dancers of Colbek* is to dissuade its hearers from certain sacrilegious behavior; while *Apollonius of Tyre* is told to make clear

> What is to love in good manere,
> And what to love in other wyse.

The three other narratives in this collection have no such declared larger purposes. Not much of a case, certainly, can be made for the tale of *Floris*, as anything except entertainment; *Ywayn and Gawayn* embodies some of the features of the courtly romance—a point of significance in itself—but the presentation of ideal chivalric behavior is severely attenuated in the English adaptation of Chrétien de Troyes' romance. If *Sir Orfeo* has a larger meaning or purpose, it is of a kind most elusive of definition, since it inheres in the elements of fantasy in the tale. In all these narratives, of course, meanings may be found through other modes of analysis. *Ywayn and Gawayn*, to take but one example, seems particularly rich in materials for psychoanalytic criticism.

One final aspect of the narratives should be mentioned if their differences from modern fiction are to be taken into account. In the sense of being plausible from the perspective of a normal perception of actuality, realism is absent from these narratives. Magic rings really have magical power—one makes Ywayn invisible, another protects him from injury, and still another keeps Floris from harm; magic wells produce violent storms or test the virginity of maidens; a giant, a compassionate (almost human) lion, the king of faery, miraculous medicines, a year-long carole (dance) are matter-of-factly mentioned; disguises, tricks, and stratagems are as foolproof as they are farfetched—and so on and on. It is hardly necessary to add that geography and chronometry subserve the plot rather than impose upon it. Yet the handling of unsystematic place and time is less a problem in narrative than in drama, and even there it is manageable, as medieval plays and some of Shakespeare's later plays, for example, affirm. Whatever "truth" there may be in these narratives, then, will be other than a representational kind.

2. THE FIVE NARRATIVES

The narratives collected in this volume, like so many prior to Malory, have long stood in the shadow of Chaucer. This both is and is not as it should be. *Sir Orfeo*, as has been said, is one

of the best narratives of its kind; it is better—as faery romance—
than *The Wife of Bath's Tale*. That the Wife of Bath's narration
of the tale of the Loathly Lady is by itself in some ways unat-
tractive and even repulsive (while the verbal style is kept at a
very high level) may be accounted for by Chaucer's dramatic
use of the narrative: the narrative manner befits the narrator
that Chaucer has presented before the tale is told. But Chaucer
has not elsewhere provided us with pure romance comparable
to *Sir Orfeo*. *Ywayn and Gawayn* is a better story, better told,
than some of Chaucer's romances (and his *Legends*, certainly)
and most of Gower's tales in English, as Loomis has said in *The
Development of Arthurian Romance* (p. 141); it has been
overshadowed both by Chrétien de Troyes' romances and by *Sir
Gawayn and the Green Knight*. Gower's *Apollonius of Tyre*,
along with his other tales, has not always been obscured by
Chaucer's work, it is true; but for the past three centuries
Gower has been little read and less attended to. For the other
narratives not a great deal can be claimed; they will have to
stand on what merit they do have, the historical fact of their
popularity, or as representative of the various techniques and
degrees of skills among the many in Middle English narratives.

Sir Orfeo. The three extant texts of *Sir Orfeo* were copied in
the fourteenth and fifteenth centuries—the Auchinleck MS.
about 1330, MS. Harley 3910 in the early 1400's, and MS. Ashmole 61 in the late 1400's. All three manuscripts are compila-
tions that include moral and religious pieces, and two contain
other romances. The Auchinleck MS., in which there is also a
version of *Floris and Blancheflour*, was probably produced
commercially in a London bookshop and may at one time have
belonged to Chaucer. In the present collection, a few selected
parallels, printed as footnotes, illustrate variations among these
texts. The Auchinleck text, though the earliest and evidently
the best, does not represent an original composition. Although
it appears to be a fairly close copy, linguistic evidence indi-
cates that *Sir Orfeo* was first written in English in the second
half of the thirteenth century, probably as a translation from an

Old French or Anglo-Norman text. Absence of direct evidence prevents more positive or extensive statements about the origin and authoritative text of the English poem.

It is clear enough from the three versions, however, that transmission and composition of the poem can never be altogether separated. The texts vary in length from about 600 lines (Auchinleck and Ashmole) to 509 lines (Harley); although the two longer versions are of about equal length, the Ashmole version has more than fifty new lines scattered throughout, while omitting about the same number found in the Auchinleck version, and several lines are transposed. The rhymes—sometimes made with mere tags—also point to transmission with recomposition, as some of the parallels witness. Once the verse narrative of *Orfeo* was written in English in the late 1200's, it seems not only to have been copied, but also to have been told from memory, probably by popular entertainers, whose talent for improvisation made good any lapses of memory.

"*Sir Orfeo* is nearly perfect as an English representative of the 'Breton lay' " (Ker, p. 94). The attractiveness of *Sir Orfeo* as literature, however, has proved as difficult to account for as it is generally acknowledged. Certainly the poem's three-part structure, its unity and economy, and its control of the faery element are carefully wrought. In the prologue (lines 1–56), for instance, "the reader is told everything that is vital to his understanding of the story, and nothing that is superfluous" (Bliss, p. xli). At the same time, as Kane points out (p. 81), the poem is "a strange mixture of moments of great roughness or banality and moments of sensitivity." It has a number of technical shortcomings not unlike those in several other romances that are regularly regarded as failures. (One cannot help being disturbed, for example, by the total predictability of the rhyme *nome: come*—alone or in compounds or with prefixes.) But in any anatomy of success, perhaps there is no better approach than to regard the poem steadily as a construction in literary—linguistic—art. The fable may have an intrinsic charm, the structure may be unified and well proportioned, the empirical and the imaginary may be separately or jointly acceptable, and so on through the critical checklist. Yet it is only in the particular literary construction, executed as words in a given conjunction, that artistic merit can be assessed. For *Sir Orfeo*, as for other tales and romances, it is the particular narration that succeeds or does not. One need only compare this version to those in the other two manuscripts (or compare this romance to others in this collection) to perceive immediately the dependence of literary merit on the totality of the verbal construction. Its flaws detract from the aesthetic effect of the poem, to be sure, leaving an impression of something less than full artistic inevitability; they occur principally in diction and seem never to have been altogether avoided in the English versions. That *Sir Orfeo* has proved attractive to modern as well as to medieval readers, however, attests to its inherent literary qualities, whatever its antecedents or potential may have been.

The text that follows is based on that established for the Auchinleck version in the edition by A. J. Bliss, and includes his emendations and reconstruction of the first thirty-eight lines.

The Cursed Dancers of Colbek. This narrative occurs in Robert Mannyng of Brunne's *Handlyng Synne* (lines 8987–9252), a translation-adaptation of William of Wadington's *Manuel de Pechiez*. Mannyng's title is perhaps the least skillful part of the translation, and he quite cumbersomely explicates it:

> In Frenshe ther a clerk it sees,
> He clepeth° it "Manuel de Pecches."
> 'Manuel' is 'handlyng wyth honde';
> 'Pecches' is 'synne,' I understonde.
> Thise two wordes that ben a-twynne†
> Do hem togidre, is "Handlyng Synne."
> (Lines 81–86)

° **clepeth** calls.
† **a-twynne** apart, separate.

The two complete manuscripts of *Handlyng Synne* are MS. Harley 1701 and MS. Bodley 415, both later copies of the translation begun, according to Mannyng, in 1303. *The Cursed Dancers of Colbek*, however, is based on a Latin version of the story rather than on the one in the *Manuel*.

The context of the narrative of *The Cursed Dancers* may be described briefly. The manual of sins, in both French and English versions, proceeds in systematic fashion through the Ten Commandments, the Seven Deadly Sins, sacrilege, the sacraments, and the graces of shrift. Illustrative stories for the various items comprise a full share of the more than twelve thousand lines of *Handlyng Synne*. The tales are of many kinds, from Biblical stories to events in the lives of saints and local personages. Mannyng's version describes the contents this way:

> Tales shalt thou fynde ther-inne,
> And chaunces* that have happed for synne;
> Merveils, some as I fond writen,
> And othres that have ben seen and witen;†
> Non ben ther-inne, more ne lesse,
> But that I fond write, or hadde wytnesse.
> (Lines 131–136)

Some are marvels, to be sure: the adulterous wife whose skeleton split in two; the witch and her cow-sucking bag; a priest who could read people's sins in their faces; marvelous tales of visions and temptations or tales of usurers, hermits, dishonest executors. A number are hardly tales at all, but merely notable "events" summarily recounted; these are particularly relevant to the account of the Dancers of Colbek. One such, told under the heading of the Fourth Deadly Sin, Sloth, resembles the story of the Dancers very closely in its subject matter. It concerns a minstrel admitted out of charity to a pious bishop's house; the minstrel disturbed the bishop's blessing of the food

---

* **chaunces** events, happenings.
† **witen** known.

by his "melodye . . . loude and hy," and the bishop foresaw
the vengeance that would befall the minstrel on his departure:

> And as he passed out at the yate,*
> A ston fel doun of the wal
> And slought† ther the mynstral.
> (Lines 4726–8)

The entire account is rendered in twenty-eight lines, followed
by an explication of its meaning. Another "tale," told immediately preceding *The Cursed Dancers of Colbek* as one of the
illustrations of sacrilege, concerns a husband and wife who fled
their enemies and were granted a chamber in an abbey; God
was not pleased that the husband "knew his wyf / Of flesshly
dede" so near the church, and so wrought that "They myghte no
more be broght a-sonder"; prayers of the monks soon brought
forgiveness. All this is set forth in about three dozen lines. In
the *Manuel* the story of the Cursed Dancers was also told in
this summary fashion, in just over fifty lines; it is this that
Mannyng developed into a proper, if short, narrative by turn-
ing to a Latin version of the tale. The refrain of the Dancers'
carole, "Why stonde we? Why gon we noght?"–taken directly
from the Latin, "Quid stamus? Cur non imus?"–provides some
excellent irony for Mannyng's narrative.

The text that follows is based on Sisam's edition of the narrative in *Fourteenth Century Verse and Prose.*

Apollonius of Tyre. John Gower's narrative of Apollonius is
the final tale (Book VIII, lines 271–2008) in his very long
framed collection of tales, *Confessio Amantis,* written near the
end of the fourteenth century. The story is ostensibly told to
illustrate the laws of marriage. In introducing *Apollonius of
Tyre* Gower explains the tale's purpose:

---

* **yate** gate.
† **slough** struck dead.

... Every man is othres lore;*
Of that† bifel in tyme er this
The present tyme which now is
May ben enformed how it stood,
And take that him thynketh good,
And leve that which is noght so.
But for-to loke of tyme go,‡
How lust of love excedeth lawe,
It oghte for-to ben wythdrawe;
For every man it sholde drede
And namely in his sibrede,**
Which turneth ofte to vengeaunce:
Wher-of a tale in remembraunce,
Which is a long proces to here,††
I thenke for-to telle here.

(Book VIII, lines 256–70)

The context of the tale does not, however, account for either
the shape of the story or the manner of its telling.

The narrative of Apollonius is indeed "a long proces to
here." The action itself is lengthy and cannot very well be
abridged if Gower is to remain faithful to the familiar tale; if
one begins to wonder, for example, why Apollonius takes a sea
voyage bound to be disastrous whenever the plot has come
to a point of stasis, the fault lies in the structure of Gower's
model, and there is little he seems able to do about it. Gower's
style, moreover, expands the narrative: the eight syllables of
his verse line cannot advance the story very much, enhance
the description, deepen the significance of the tale, when a
fourth to a half of the syllables are taken up with conjunctions and adverbs, as is so often the case. The effects of be-

* **lore** teaching, example.
† **that** i.e., that which.
‡ **go** gone.
** **sibrede** kindred.
†† **here** hear.

ginning such a high proportion of lines with words of these grammatical classes are several. The "flow" of the narrative is exceedingly smooth, because all assertions and qualifiers, all events and details, have their relations explicitly stated. The pace of the narrative is casual. Monotony, however, is now and again unavoidable. (Because such a high proportion of clauses begin with conjunctions, the punctuation of the text by modern standards is very difficult, and occasionally it is perforce arbitrary.) There are correlates of this characteristic of verbal style in the fact that few of the obvious—usually interim—actions are left unstated, to be inferred automatically. When, for example, a strange ship appears offshore near a company of people,

> To knowe what it mene may,
> Til it be come they abide.

Altogether, Gower's narrative "is a clear, if shallow, stream, rippling pleasantly over the stones and unbroken either by dams or cataracts" (Macaulay, I, xii). It may be added that shifts in the narration between past-tense and present-tense predicates—even within coordinate construction—are Gower's doing.

The text is based on G. C. Macaulay's edition of *The English Works of John Gower*.

Floris and Blancheflour. Although four texts of this popular romance survive, none are complete. The two early ones, Cambridge MS. Gg. 4.27.2 and Cotton Vitellius D. iii, were written in the thirteenth century. One text is in the Auchinleck MS.; another text was copied in the fifteenth century, in Egerton MS. 2862. All the texts are copies or perhaps revisions.

Probably none of the other narratives in this collection exemplify so clearly the regrettable effects of translation as it was often practiced in the post-Norman era of England. The love story of Floris and Blancheflour is difficult to sustain, at best, and its happy ending surely lessens our interest in the tale

—much as we might feel if *Romeo and Juliet* ended happily. Floris' disregard of all save his passion for his beloved and his rather repetitive "muchel wo" do not induce us to feel very much affection or sympathy for him, while Blancheflour is little more than the passive object of his passion. It is difficult to regard the hero and heroine, even at the climax of the story, as we apparently should:

> Ther was non so sterne man
> That the children loked on,
> That they ne wolde, al wel fawe,°
> Her juggement have wythdrawe,
> And wyth greet catel hem beye,†
> If they durste speke or seye:
> For Floris was so faire a yongelyng‡
> And Blancheflour so swete a thynge. . . .

It is the plot, or its embellishments, or both, on which the interest could most readily have been centered, and the original narrative was supplied with these matters aplenty. The extant English versions, nonetheless, do too little justice to the adventures of Floris and Blancheflour or the wonders of the East. They are indeed mentioned—they are the substance of the tale; yet the translation and its reworkings have neither the verse quality, nor the interpretive depth, nor even, in general, the ingenuousness (as in *Sir Orfeo*) to realize the potential of this tale. The fact that in some sections of the extant texts there are flashes of economy and a winning ingenuousness, however, does suggest that there may have been a superior English version of the tale that has not come down to us. One short section offers several illustrations of that superior touch. Clarys teasingly asks her chamber-mate Blancheflour to come and see the basket of flowers in which Blancheflour's lover has

° **fawe** willingly.
† **catel** wealth; **beye** redeem.
‡ **yongelyng** youth.

been smuggled into her chamber; in one version Clarys says simply,

> "Go we see that ilke flour."

but in another the verbiage diminishes the effect:

> "Blancheflour," she seyde, "go we y-fere*,
> Leve swete Blancheflour,
> Com and see a wel faire flour."

When the lovers leap together in an embrace, they kiss (according to one version) "wonder swete," or (according to another) "and eke wepe," but the virtue of the first version is achieved at the expense of the rhyme. Clarys then asks (charmingly),

> "Felawe, knowest thou oght this flour?"

or (heavy-handedly):

> "Knowest thou oght yet this flour?
> A litel erre thou noldest† it see;
> Now ne myghte it lete‡ from thee."

In an earlier section the narrator-redactor has used excellent economy by having the Emir's fortress-harem described to Floris and the strategy to gain entry fully outlined for him, and then in four lines (lines 705–8) simply declaring that Floris successfully carried out the plan. Yet the great appetite for stories in English that made Gower so popular and brought forth so many translations of independent works found generally rough fare in the extant texts of this tale. Symptoms of the carelessness with which the texts were composed abound in lines that are too short, too long, or without rhyme, and in tags which, if not meaningless, are insignificant or anomalous. The variations among the texts appear to be those of careless or inept translators, redactors, and copyists, not of minstrels.

---

* **y-fere** together.
† **noldest** would not.
‡ **lete** let go, release.

It may be remarked that the present editor, having worked long enough with Middle English verse to have a certain empathy with copyist-translators of the fourteenth century, felt a strong temptation (and more strongly resisted it) to rewrite lines of the tale of Floris as freely as did the writers of the surviving texts: at least the verse could be improved and the story given a better chance.

The text is based on the Egerton MS., edited by George H. McKnight, in *King Horn, Floriz and Blauncheflour, The Assumpton of Our Lady*.

Ywayn and Gawayn. Chrétien de Troyes' *Yvain* became, in English, *Ywayn and Gawayn*. The unique text is in MS. Cotton Galba E. ix, of the fourteenth century; it appears to be a copy of a translation made before or about 1350. The English narrative follows Chrétien de Troyes' entire story incident by incident, often speech by speech. The translator, however, rendered the story with a difference, as briefly described earlier. The variations may be discovered in detail by comparing the present version with the French romance, translations of which may be readily obtained (see Bibliographic Notes).

As a story of knightly adventure, *Ywayn and Gawayn* is carefully plotted (following Chrétien) and competently executed. A few flaws resulting from abridgment of the longer French version occur, but none are particularly troublesome to the plot. There appears to be one passage in which the copyist preserved half a dozen lines that should have been canceled (lines 1561–6 and lines 1567–72 are probably alternate versions of the same material); the text is nevertheless complete, and carefully composed and copied. Moreover, this narrative has all the advantages that the English *Floris and Blauncheflour* lost in the hands of its translator and redactors, along with a swiftness and force lacking in Gower's narrative style.

It may be noted that Gawayn is named in the title not because he has a part equal to Ywayn's in the action (though Gawayn does participate in the climactic combat), but because, apparently, his popularity in English narratives—far exceeding that of Ywayn—prompted the translator to name him in the hope of attracting a greater audience to read and hear again this story.

The text is based on the recent edition by Albert B. Friedman and Norman T. Harrington.

3. NORMALIZATION, LANGUAGE, AND METER

All the texts in this edition have been normalized to a (literary) dialect reconstructed from London–East Midland writings of about 1400. The purpose and procedures of linguistic normalization parallel those of *One Hundred Middle English Lyrics*,[1] and may be summarized briefly. The linguistic diversity among Middle English texts reflects the linguistic diversity of speech and the lack of a standard literary language. Speech sounds and spellings, especially, varied widely from dialect to dialect, and to some extent the morphology and vocabulary varied as well. Texts in Middle English, consequently, have been inaccessible for most practical purposes to general readers and undergraduates. In effect, the narratives, like the lyrics, could be read only by those who first served an apprenticeship to English philology or who were willing to pause frequently to consult a glossary. Translations into Modern English have been neither plentiful nor regularly successful. The dialectal variations in spelling of forms—whether words, word roots, or inflections—were to a great extent systematic variations, so that normalization is feasible. Most variations in morphology may be eliminated by normalization, with only occasional interference with the meter or rhyme; if the effect is serious, the original form is retained and glossed. Vocabulary cannot ordinarily be normalized in metered texts without rewriting at least

---

[1] *One Hundred Middle English Lyrics*, ed. Robert D. Stevick (Indianapolis and New York: Bobbs-Merrill, 1964).

an entire line (a procedure of translation); hence no change in the words and their sequence is made in the way of normalization, and glosses are provided. Normalization may be distinguished from emendation as follows: Normalization consists of reshaping morphemes of a text in one dialect to conform to the shape of their correlatives in another and, in some inflections, using the expected allomorphs (i.e., alternate forms of a morpheme) of one dialect in place of those occurring in texts from another dialect; and adoption of a stable spelling practice (uniform morphographs). "þat ȝe cumand him to say / And tel forth, als he had tyght" becomes "That ye comaunde him to seye / And telle forth, as he hadde tyght"; "& ȝif þou makest ous y-let" becomes "And if thou makest us y-let." Emendation consists of addition, deletion, or substitution with respect to the sequence of morphemes in a specific text. Except for minor substitutions such as *but* for *ac*, emendations are recorded in footnotes; it should be noted, though, that only departures from the edited text listed for each narrative are thus footnoted. The procedures of normalization, in short, produce a set of texts with sufficient uniformity of linguistic (and orthographic) features to make the texts readily accessible in Middle English to nonspecialists. Modern punctuation, as usual, is supplied by the editor. But for the accidents of history the texts here printed might have been produced in something like their present form by a younger contemporary of Chaucer and Gower.

Details of the procedure of normalization need not be repeated from the Introduction to *One Hundred Middle English Lyrics*. It may be useful, however, to include here a brief description of the morphology and the phonological-orthographic correspondences for these texts.

In this edition, the paradigmatic classes are uniformly represented. The morphological descriptions that follow resemble those drawn up for Chaucer's works, for example, W. W. Skeat's Oxford *Chaucer*, Vol. VI.

A. *Personal Pronouns*

I	my, myn	me
thou, -ow	thy, thyn	thee
he	his,	him
she	hir, hires	hire
it	his	it
we	oure, oures	us
ye	youre, youres	you
they	her, heres	hem

All pairs are used here in complementary distribution. *My / myn* and *thy / thyn* are distributed according to the initial sound of the following word if it is part of the same phrase: *my lyf, my joye, myn owene lady dere, thy fon*, and also *myn herte, thyn honour*. When not preceding the noun they modify, *myn, thyn, oures, youres, heres, hires* are usual forms.

B. *Nouns*

{Ø}	oon sone	oon flour	that preest
{S₁}	three sones	three floures	tho prestes
{S₂}	his sones sorwe	the floures savour	the prestes bedes

The first member of this paradigm {Ø} (i.e., no suffix) is the singular morpheme, contrasting with {S₁}, the plural morpheme; {S₂} is variously called "genitive," "determinative," "possessive." As many infrequent inflectional allomorphs are eliminated in the texts as evidence and structure of the poetic line permit. Occasionally, however, a fourth member of the paradigm occurs, often in frequent or formulaic phrases corresponding to Old English dative inflections; it has the shape /-ə/ *-e*, as in *wyth childe, in boure, to grounde*. Also, the plural morpheme {S₁}, which nearly always has the shape /-əs/, included allomorphs /-(ə)n/ *-(e)n* and /Ø/. These occurred with some frequency, as in Chaucer's *eyen* "eyes," for example. Consequently, *-(e)n* plurals, e.g., *fon* "foes," are retained when rhyme requires them. *Thyng* is a frequent instance of plural with /Ø/ inflection and cannot always be replaced by *thynges*, as in *alle thyng* rhymed with *kyng*.

A few double forms of roots occur, such as *wyl, wylle;* usually these forms continue double forms that had occurred in Old English.

C. *Adjectives*

Generally, monosyllabic adjectives, *myn, thyn,* and a few others, show the following inflectional characteristics:

a good man
the/that/thy gode man
Come, gode man, . . .
gode men

thyn hond	al my lyf	swich a dede
thyne hondes	alle her lyves	swiche dedes

D. *Verbs*

The personal inflections of verbs need not be listed here in full, since they are regular and offer no difficulty, but the plural *-en* (alternating with *-e*) may be mentioned. Tense inflections, similarly, correspond closely to those of Modern English; exceptions are those of some "strong" verbs, and these are listed and cross-referenced in the Glossary. In nearly every instance, verbs with both strong and weak forms have been made either strong or weak. The forms of anomalous and irregular verbs are also given in the Glossary. Modal inflections are as follows. Imperative singular Ø (no suffix), or *-e* for some weak verbs, plural *-(e)th*, rarely *-e*. Present subjunctive singular *-e*, plural *-e(n)*; preterite subjunctive is similar, except that there may be no inflectional suffix after *-(e)d*. Infinitive inflections are *-e* or *-en*. Participial forms are sufficiently similar to those of Modern English to cause no difficulty. The past participial prefix is regularly *i-*, and the general (vestigial) verbal prefix is regularly *y-*.

E. *Adverbs, prepositions, particles, demonstrative and interrogative pronouns.*

These, if not closely similar to those of Modern English, are listed in the Glossary.

Whether or not the phonetic reconstructions of Middle English dialects correspond exactly to the speech of the time, it is necessary to have some pronunciation system in order to read Middle English texts fluently. A pronunciation system that is deliberately designed to reflect the phonemic structure of the stipulated dialect is preferable to most improvisations of users of Modern English only. On these grounds, the following guide is offered.

The consonants are these:

/p/	pere, hap	*as Mod. E.*	*peer*
/t/	tere, but		*tear*
/č/	chere, wrecched		*cheer*
/k/	kyn, care, quene, sak, six		*kin*
/f/	fere, staf		*staff*
/θ/	this, lieth		*thin*
/s/	so, certeyn, faste, lesse, six		*so*
/š/	sholde, fresshe, flessh		*should*
/b/	bere, aboute, neb		*bear*
/d/	dere, adoun, bed		*dear*
/ǰ/	daunger, juggement		*judge*
/g/	gon, ageyn		*go*
/v/	vois, staves		*voice*
/ð/	blithe		*blithe*
/z/	lese		*lose*
/x/	soghte, thoght, thogh		————
/h/	here, herte		*hear*
/w/	were, sorwe		*were*
/m/	mere, am		*mill*
/l/	lere, al		*like*
/j/	yeer, ayeins		*year*
/n/	nere, an, signe		*near*
/r/	rede, bour		*rear*

It should be noticed that /ŋ/ and /ž/ as in Modern English *sing* and *azure* were not phonemic in Middle English, and that /x/ is not part of the Modern English phonemic system.[2] Double consonant letters indicate lengthened consonants; in some instances, such as *sone* "son," *sonne* "sun," length is phonemic.

The chart, p. xxxii, which draws heavily on Chapter IV of Samuel Moore's *Historical Outlines of English Sounds and Inflections* (revised by Albert H. Marckwardt, 1951) and Chapter 43 of Charles F. Hockett's *A Course in Modern Linguistics* (1958), offers a correlation between the stressed vowels of the texts and those of Modern English that may be helpful.

Word stress, when different from that of corresponding Modern English forms, can be inferred from the metrical stress patterns.

Finally, some remarks on the meter of these texts. It is customary to describe the metrical form for all these narratives as "octosyllabic couplets." The generalization should not be allowed to obscure the variation in metrical characteristics of the individual texts, however, for the differences are not difficult to observe and are of considerable interest. Gower's narrative is probably the only one of the five best described as being in octosyllabic couplets: he writes strict eight-syllable lines rhymed in pairs. His rhymes are exact. The only license he takes is in alternating forms of words to keep the exactness of meter and rhyme: *there* appears instead of *ther* when it rhymes, for example, with an infinitive, *awey* alternates with *aweye*, *out* with *oute*, *go* with *gon*, *to ship* sometimes has -(*p*)*e* added, etc. Gower writes in paragraph units independent of number of couplets and usually places his paragraph division in the middle of a couplet. The other texts are better described as using short four-stress lines rhymed in couplets: normally, stressed syllables have one, sometimes two, occasionally three or more syllables intervening, and lines frequently begin with a stressed syllable. It is neither convenient nor useful to describe the variety in syl-

---

[2] /x/ is distinguished phonetically as a voiceless velar or palatal spirant. Roughly, as [t] is to [θ], so [k] is to [x].

Phoneme	Spelling	Pronunciation	as in	If Modern English has	as in
/i/	i, y	[ɪ]	drynke, bidde	[ɪ]	drink, bid
/e/	e	[ɛ]	helpe	[ɛ]	help
/a/	a	[a]	can	[æ]	can
/o/	o	[ɔ]	oxe	[a]	ox
/u/	u, o	[ʊ]*	under, sone	[ʌ]	under, son
/iy/	i, y	[i:]	side, wyf	[aɪ]	side, wife
/ey/	e, ee	[e:]*	swete, feet	[i:]	sweet, feet
/ay/	ai, ay, ei, ey	[æɪ]*	day, pleye	[e] or [eɪ]	day, play
/oy/	oi, oy	[ɔɪ]	boy, vois	[ɔɪ]	boy, voice
/iw/	u, eu, ew	[ɪʊ] or [ɛʊ]	pure, newe	[ɪu, u] or [ju]	pure, new
/aw/	o, ou, ow, au, aw	[ɔʊ] or [aʊ]	thoght, taughte, saw	[ɔ]	thought, taught, saw
/ow/	o, oo	[o:]*	fode, mood	[u]	food, mood
/uw/	ou, ow	[u:]*	hous	[aʊ]	house
/eh/	e, ee	[æ:]*	lede, seed	[i:]	lead, seed
/ah/	a, au	[a:]*	name, aungel	[e]	name, angel
/oh/	o, ou	[ɔ:]*	bon, soule	[o]	bone, soul

* [ʊ] as in Modern English *full*; [æɪ] is a glide of the sounds indicated, with stress on the first element; the other vowels are lengthened counterparts (shown by: after the letter) of [e, o, u, æ, a, ɔ], the vowels of Modern English *day, bone, food, can, ox, thought.*

lable pattern as deviation or substitution or irregularity within "octosyllabic couplets." Mannyng's verse often appears more regular in the normalized text than in the original text; but its foundation is in number of full stresses rather than number of syllables, as can be observed, for example, in the nine one-syllable words making up line 143 of *The Cursed Dancers of Colbek,* or the imperative to elision in line 207. Mannyng apparently had no hesitation in alternating forms of words to accommodate rhyme (e.g. *wore / were*) or meter. The unit of exposition is predominantly four lines, two pairs of couplets. *Sir Orfeo* has an accentual meter that approaches regular octosyllabics as well; it provides a particularly interesting set of variations. For instance, parallel constructions beginning *he that . . .* read in the Auchinleck MS. text as follows: *hadde ben* (235), *hadde y-wered* (241), *hadde had* (245), *had y-had* (249, 253); *made* and *makede* alternate in the same text; *Orfewe* (24) and *Orfeo* (120) are rhymed differently; *to-tore* alternates with *to-torn, bihold* with *biholden* (participles), *hed* with *hade* "head" (rhymed with *red* and *nade*), *opon* with *opan* (rhymed with *anon* and *man*). Its unit of composition is the paragraph ending in a completed couplet. *Ywayn and Gawayn,* more than any of the other narratives in this collection, uses alliteration. The accentual basis of the verse is even more prominent for that reason; yet it, too, allows close approximation of octosyllabics. The contrast between the meter of *Ywayn and Gawayn* and that of *Apollonius of Tyre,* however, is extremely marked. In the narrative of *Ywayn* the stresses are placed by the patterns of both word stress and phrase stress, while in Gower's narrative these patterns of stress are not particularly observed.

Bibliographic Notes

Bibliographic help is generally available in John E. Wells, *A Manual of the Writings in Middle English, 1050–1400* (New Haven, 1916), with supplements, and in the annual bibliography published in *PMLA* (Publications of the Modern Language Association of America). A survey of the narrative and romance materials in Middle English, with some bibliographic notes, may be found in *A Literary History of England*, ed. Albert C. Baugh (New York, 1948), *A History of English Literature*, ed. Hardin Craig (New York, 1950), or, more recently, David M. Zesmer, *Guide to English Literature from Beowulf through Chaucer and Medieval Drama* (New York, 1961); the last-named book contains a very good selected bibliography, with annotations, by Stanley B. Greenfield. Dorothy Everett's "A Characterization of the English Medieval Romance" is reprinted in her *Essays on Middle English Literature*, ed. Patricia Kean (Oxford, 1955).

Textual sources for the narratives included in this edition are as follows:

Sir Orfeo, ed. A. J. Bliss (Oxford, 1954). Besides full texts, notes and glossaries for the three extant versions of the narrative, this edition contains a full Introduction treating the sources and literary qualities of the poem, as well as the important features of the manuscripts and language.

The Cursed Dancers of Colbek in *Fourteenth Century Verse and Prose*, ed. Kenneth Sisam (Oxford, 1948). A complete text of *Handlyng Synne* may be found in *Robert of Brunne's "Handlyng Synne . . . ,"* ed. Frederick J. Furnivall (London, 1901, 1903; EETS O.S. 119, 123).

Apollonius of Tyre in *The English Works of John Gower*, ed. G. C. Macaulay, 2 vols. (London, 1900–1901; EETS E.S. 81–82). These volumes also form part of Macaulay, ed., *The Works of John Gower*, 4 vols. (Oxford, 1899–1902).

Floris and Blancheflour, in *King Horn, Floriz and Blaunche-flour, The Assumption of Our Lady*, ed. George H. McKnight

(London, 1901; a re-edition of EETS O.S. 14). An edition based on the Auchinleck MS., with additional lines from the other MSS, is *Floris and Blancheflour: A Middle English Romance,* ed. A. B. Taylor (Oxford, 1927).

Ywayn and Gawayn, ed. Albert E. Friedman and Norman T. Harrington (London, 1964; EETS O.S., 254). A full edition with introductory notes on the manuscript, its relation to Chrétien de Troyes' *Yvain,* language, structure, etc., a commentary, and glossary.

Also cited in the Introduction are the following:

Hockett, Charles F. *A Course in Modern Linguistics.* New York, 1958.

Kane, George. *Middle English Literature.* London, 1951. (Part I is "The Middle English Metrical Romances.")

Ker, W. P. *Epic and Romance.* 2nd ed. London, 1908 (reissued New York, 1958).

Loomis, Roger Sherman. *The Development of Arthurian Romance.* London, 1963.

Moore, Samuel. *Historical Outlines of English Sounds and Inflections,* rev. Albert H. Marckwardt. Ann Arbor, 1951.

To these may be added:

Baugh, Albert C. "The Middle English Romance: Some Questions of Creation, Presentation, and Preservation," *Speculum,* LXII (1967), 1-31.

Chrétien de Troyes: Arthurian Romances, trans. and ed. W. W. Comfort. Everyman Library. New York, 1914 (Contains *Yvain.*)

Hibbard [Loomis], Laura A. *Medieval Romance in England....* New York, 1924.

French, Walter Hoyt, and Hale, Charles Brockway, eds. *Middle English Metrical Romances,* New York, 1930. (Contains *Sir Orfeo, Ywayn and Gawayn* [selection], and *Floris and Blancheflour.*)

Loomis, Roger S. and Laura H., eds. *Medieval Romances.* New York, 1957. (Contains translations, with introductions; includes *Sir Orfeo.*)

Sands, Donald B., ed. *Middle English Verse Romances.* New York, 1966. (Includes *Sir Orfeo* and *Floris and Blanche-flour.*)

Ywain, The Knight of the Lion, trans. Robert W. Ackerman and Frederick W. Locke. New York, 1957.

TEXTS OF THE NARRATIVES

Sir Orfeo

The Cursed Dancers of Colbek

Apollonius of Tyre

Floris and Blancheflour

Ywayn and Gawayn

Sir Orfeo

We reden ofte and fynde i-write,
And thise clerkes wel it wite,+
Layes that ben in harpyng+
Ben i-founde of ferly+ thyng.
5   Som beth of werre+ and som of wo,
And som of joye and myrthe also,
And som of trecherie and of gile,
Of olde aventures that felle while,+
And som of bourdes and ribaudye,+
10   And many ther beth of fairye;+
Of alle thynges that men seen,
Moste of love, for sothe, they ben.
    In Britayne+ thise layes were wroght
(First i-founde and forth i-broght)
15   Of aventures that felle by dayes+
Wher-of Britons maden her layes.
Whan kynges myghte o-wher y-here+
Of any merveils that ther were,
They toke an harpe in glee and game
20   And maden a lay and yave it name.
Now of thise aventures that were i-falle
I can telle some, but not alle.
But herkneth, lordynges that ben trewe,

---

2 **wite** know.
3 **harpyng** minstrelsy.
4 **ferly** marvelous, wondrous.
5 **werre** war.
8 **while** formerly.
9 **bourdes and ribaudye** jests and ribaldry.
10 **fairye** faery, fairyland.
13 **Britayne** Brittany.
15 **by dayes** i.e., once upon a time.
17 **o-wher y-here** hear anywhere.

3

I wyl you telle "Sir Orfewe."
25 Orfeo, moste of any thyng,
    Loved the glee of harpyng;
    Siker was every good harpour+
    Of him to have muche honour.
    Himself he lerned for-to harpe
30 And leyde ther-on his wyttes sharpe;
    He lerned so ther no-thyng+ was
    A bettre harpour in no place.
    In al the world was no man born
    That ones Orfeo sat biforn,
35 An+ he myghte of his harpyng here,
    But he sholde thenke that he were
    In oon of the joyes of paradys,
    Swich melodye in his harping is.
        Orfeo was a kyng
40 In Englelond, an heighe lordyng,
    A stalworth man and hardy bo,+
    Large and curteis+ he was also.
    His fader was comen of Kyng Pluto,
    And his moder of Kyng Juno,
45 That som-tyme+ were as goddes i-holde
    For aventures that they dide and tolde.
    This kyng sojourned+ in Traciens,
    That was a citee of noble defence;+

27 **harpour** harpist, minstrel.
31 **no-thyng** not at all.
35 **An** if.
41 **bo** as well.
42 **Large and curteis** generous and gracious.
43–44 Pluto, king of Hades, regarded here (as in other works) as king of Fairyland. Only the Auchinleck MS. has Juno as a king.
45 **som-tyme** formerly.
47 **sojourned** dwelled.
47–50 Only in the Auchinleck MS. is Thrace (*Traciens*) identified with Winchester, the old capital of England.
48 **defence** fortifications.

4

For Winchester was cleped+ tho
50   Traciens wythouten no.+
      The kyng hadde a quene of pris+
    That was i-cleped Dame Heurodis;
    The faireste lady, for the nones,
    That myghte gon of body and bones;
55   Ful of love and of goodnesse—
    But no man may telle hir fairnesse.

      Biel so in the comsyng+ of May,
    Whan myrie and hot is the day,
    And awey beth wynter-shoures,
60   And every feeld is ful of floures,
    And blosme breme+ on every bough
    Over-al+ waxeth myrie ynough,
    This ilke quene, Dame Heurodis,
    Took two maydens of pris
65   And went in an undren-tide+
    To pleye by an orcherd-side,
    To see the floures sprede and sprynge,+
    And to here the foweles synge.
    They sete hem doun alle three
70   Under a faire ympe-tree,+
    And wel soon this faire quene
    Fel on sleep upon the grene.+
    The maydens durste hire not a-wake,

49 **cleped** called.
50 **wythouten no** without denial, undeniably.
51 **of pris** precious, excellent.
57 **comsyng** beginning.
61 **breme** bright, glorious.
62 **Over-al** everywhere.
65 **undren-tide** midmorning (-time).
67 **sprede and sprynge** spread (unfold) and grow.
70 **ympe-tree** grafted tree.
72 **grene** greensward.

But lette hir lie and reste take.
75 So she slep til after noon,
   That[+] undren-tide was al i-don.
   But as soon as she gan a-wake
   She cried and lothly bere[+] gan make;
   She froted[+] hir hondes and hir feet,
80 And cracched hir visage[+]—it bledde wete;
   Hir riche robe she al to-ritt,[+]
   And was reveyed[+] out of hir wyt.
   The two maydens hire biside
   Ne durste wyth hire no leng[+] abide,
85 But ronne to the paleys ful right[+]
   And tolde both squier and knight
   That her quene awede[+] wolde,
   And bade hem gon and hire at-holde.[+]
   Knightes ronne and ladies also,
90 Damyselles sixty[+] and mo.
   In the orcherd to the quene they come
   And hire up in her armes nome,[+]
   And broghte hire to bed atte laste,
   And helde hire ther fine faste.[+]

76 **That** i.e., until the time that.
78 **lothly bere** horrible outcry.
79 **froted** rubbed, tore at.
80 **cracched hir visage** scratched her face.
81 **to-ritt** tore to pieces.
82 **reveyed** driven, (?) carried away.
84 **leng** = *lenger*.
85 **right** straight (-way).
85–88 Ashmole MS. reads: *Bot went vn-to þe palys a-ȝene / And told both knyȝt & sueyn [swain] / How þat þe quen a-wey wold, / And bad them com hyr to be-hold.*
87 **awede** go mad.
88 **at-holde** restrain.
90 Sixty is an indefinite number.
92 **nome** took, seized.
94 **fine faste** very securely.

6

95   But evere she heeld in oon crie,+
     And wolde up, and aweye.
     Whan Orfeo herde that tidyng,
     Nevere him nas worse for no-thyng.+
     He cam wyth knightes tene+
100 To chambre right bifore the quene,
     And biheeld, and seyde wyth greet pitee,
     "O leve lyf, what is thee,+
     That evere yet hast ben so stille,
     And now gredest+ wonder shille?+
105 Thy body that was so white y-core+
     Wyth thy nayles is al to-tore.+
     Allas! thy rode+ that was so reed+
     Is al wan as thou were deed,
     And also thyne fyngres smale
110 Beth al blody and al pale.
     Allas! thy lufsom eyen two
     Loken so man doth on his fo.
     A! Dame, I biseche mercy.
     Lat be all this reweful cry,
115 And tel me what thee is, and how,
     And what thyng may thee helpe now."
     Tho lay she stille atte laste
     And gan to wepe swithe faste,

95 **heeld in oon crie** continued (the) one lament.
98 **Nevere him nas worse for no-thyng** it was never worse for him.
99 **tene** ten.
102 **what is thee** what is the matter with you.
102–104 Harley MS. reads: "*Swete-hert,*" *he sayde, How may þis be?* /
     —*þat euer ȝet hast ben so stylle,* / *& now criest so loude &*
     schrylle." Ashmole MS. reads: "*My leffe wyff, what ayles the,*
     / *Thou þat hast be so stylle?* / *Why cryest þou wonder*
     schylle?"
104 **gredest** cry out. **shille** shrilly.
105 **y-core** excellent.
106 **to-tore** torn terribly.
107 **rode** face, complexion. **reed** red.

7

And seyde thus the kyng to:
120   "Allas, my lord Sire Orfeo!
Sithen we first togidre were,
Ones wrothe nevere we nere;[+]
But evere I have i-loved thee
As my lyf, and so thou me.
125   But now we mote dele a-two[+]—
Do thy best, for I moot go."
"Allas," quod he, "Forlorn I am!
Whider woltow[+] go, and to whom?
Whider thou gost I wyl wyth thee,
130   And whider I go thou shalt wyth me."
"Nay, nay, Sire, that noght nis![+]
I wyl thee telle al how it is.
As I lay this undren-tide
And slep under oure orcherd-side
135   Ther come to me two faire knightes
Wel y-armed al to rightes,[+]
And bade me comen on hiyng[+]
And speke wyth her lord the kyng;
And I answerde at wordes bolde,
140   I ne dar not, ne I nolde.[+]
They prikede[+] ageyn as they mighte dryve;[+]
Tho cam her kyng also blive,[+]
Wyth an hundred knightes and mo
And damyselles an hundred also,

---

122 **nere** = *ne were.*
125 **dele a-two** part.
128 **woltow** = *wolt thou.*
131 **that noght nis** i.e., that cannot be.
136 **al to rightes** quite fittingly, properly.
137 **on hiyng** in haste.
140 **nolde** = *ne wolde.*
141 **prikede** spurred (rode). **as they mighte dryve** i.e., as fast as they could.
142 **blive** quickly.

145 Al on snow-white stedes;
    As white as milk were her wedes:
    I ne saw nevere yet bifore
    So faire creatures y-core.
    The kyng hadde a croune on heed,+
150 It nas+ of silver ne of gold reed,+
    But it was of a precious ston—
    As brighte as the sonne it shon.
    And as soon as he to me cam,
    Wolde I nolde I,+ he me nam+
155 And made me wyth him ride
    Upon a palfrey by his side;
    And broghte me to his paleys
    Wel atired in ech a weyes,+
    And shewed me castels and toures,
160 Ryveres, forestes, frith+ wyth floures,
    And his riche stedes echoon;
    And sithen me broghte ageyn hom
    Into oure owene orcherd,
    And seyde to me thus afterward,
165 'Loke, Dame, to-morwe that thou be
    Right heer under this ympe-tree,
    And than thou shalt wyth us go
    And lyve wyth us evere-mo.
    And if thou makest us y-let,+
170 Wher thou be, thou worst i-fet,+
    And to-tore+ thyne limes alle
    That no-thyng helpe thee ne shal;

149 **heed** head.
150 **nas** = *ne was.* **reed** red.
154 **Wolde I nolde I** i.e., whether I wished it or not. **nam** seized.
158 **in ech a weyes** in every way.
160 **frith** woodland, park.
169 **y-let** hindrance.
170 **worst i-fet** will be fetched.
171 **to-tore** torn to pieces.

And thogh thou best so to-torn,
Yet thou worst+ wyth us i-born.' "

175   Whan Kyng Orfeo herde this cas,
"O wey," quod he, "Allas! Allas!
Lever me were to lete+ my lyf
Thanne thus to lese the quene my wyf!"
He axed counseil at ech man,

180 But no man him helpe ne can.
A-morwe the undren-tide is come,
And Orfeo hath his armes i-nome,
And wel ten hundred knightes wyth him,
Ech i-armed, stout and grym;+

185 And wyth the quene wente they
Right unto that ympe-tree.
They made sheltrom+ in ech a side,
And seyde they wolde ther abide
And deye ther everichoon

190 Er the quene sholde from hem gon.
But yet amiddes hem ful right
The quene was awey i-twight,+
Wyth fairye+ forth i-nome—
Men wiste nevere wher she was bicome.

195 Tho was ther criyng, wepe, and wo;
The kyng into his chambre is go
And ofte swoned upon the ston,
And made swich dol+ and swich mone
That nigh his lyf was i-spent—

---

174 **worst** = *worthest* will be.
177 **Lever me were to lete** I would rather forsake.
184 **grym** fearsome.
187 **sheltrom** rank of armed men.
192 **i-twight** snatched.
193 **fairye** magic, enchantment.
197–199 Ashmole MS. reads: *And oft he knelyd onne þe ston, / And made grete sorow for sche was gon.*
198 **dol** lamentation.

200 Ther was non amendement.+
He cleped togidre his barouns,
Erles, lordes of renouns,
And whan they al i-comen were,
"Lordynges," he seyde, "before you here
205 I ordeyne myn heighe styward+
To wite+ my kyngdom afterward.
In my stede ben he shal
To kepe my londes over-al.
For, now I have my quene i-lorn,
210 The faireste lady that evere was born,
Nevere eft I nyl+ no womman see.
Into wildernesse, I wyl tee,+
And lyve ther evermore
Wyth wilde bestes in holtes hore.+
215 And whan ye understonde that I be spent,
Maketh you than a parlement
And cheseth you+ a newe kyng.
Now doth youre beste wyth alle my thyng."

Tho was ther wepyng in the halle
220 And greet cry among hem alle:
Unethe+ myghte olde or yonge
For wepyng speke a word wyth tonge.

200 **amendment** remedy.
202 *renouns,* an inflected adjective, apparently modeled on the French original.
205 **styward** steward.
206 **wite** rule.
211 **nyl** = *ne wyl.*
212 **tee** go, withdraw.
214 **in holtes hore** in (the) grey woods.
215 *understonde,* as Sisam notes, overloads the line and may take the place of *wite* or *wiste.*
217 **cheseth you** choose (for) yourselves.
221 **Unethe** scarcely.

They knelede adoun alle y-fere+
And preyde him, if his wylle were,
225 That he ne sholde noght from hem go.
"Do wey!"+ quod he, "It shal be so!"
Al his kyngdom he forsook,
But a sclavin+ on him he took.
He ne hadde kirtel+ ne hood,
230 Sherte, ne non other good;
But his harpe he took algate+
And dide him barfoot out at the yate.+
No man moste wyth him go.
O wey! What! ther was wepe and wo
235 Whan he that hadde ben kyng wyth croune
Went so pourely out of toune!
Thurgh wode and over heeth
Into the wildernesse he geth.+
No-thyng he fint+ that him is ese,
240 But evere he lyveth in greet malese.+
He that hadde i-wered the fowe and grys,+
And on bed the purpre bis,+
Now on hard heeth he lieth;
Wyth leves and gras he him wryeth.+
245 He that hadde had castels and toures
Ryver, forest, frith wyth floures,

223 **y-fere** together.
226 **Do wey!** enough! have done!
228 **sclavin** pilgrim's mantle.
229 **kirtel** kirtle, short coat.
231 **algate** at any rate.
232 **yate** gate.
238 **geth** = *goth.*
239 **fint** = *fyndeth.*
240 **malese** discomfort.
241 **fowe and grys** variegated and gray furs.
242 **purpre bis** precious cloth.
244 **wryeth** wraps, covers.

Now, thogh it comse⁺ to snewe and frese,
This kyng moot make his bed in mese.⁺
He that hadde had knightes of pris
250   Bifore him knelynge, and ladies,
Now seeth he no-thyng that him liketh;
But wilde wormes⁺ by him striketh.⁺
He that hadde i-had plentee
Of mete and drynke, of ech deyntee,⁺
255   Now may he al-day digge and wrote⁺
Er he fynde his fille of rote.
In somer he lyveth by wilde fruyt
And beryes but gode lite;
In wynter may he no-thyng fynde
260   But rote, grases, and the rynde.⁺
Al his body was awey dwyned⁺
For misese,⁺ and al to-chined.⁺
Lord! who may telle the sore
This kyng suffred ten yere and more?
265   His heer of his berd, blak and rowe,⁺
To his girdel-stede⁺ was growe.
His harpe wher-on was al his glee,
He hidde in an holwe tree;
And whan the weder was clere and bright
270   He took his harpe to him wel right
And harped at his owene wylle.
Into al the wode the soun gan shille,⁺

---

247 **comse** begins.
248 **mese** moss.
252 **wormes** serpents. **striketh** glide.
254 **deyntee** delicacy.
255 **wrote** grub, root (in the ground).
260 **rynde** bark, husks.
261 **dwyned** shrunk, wasted.
262 **misese** discomfort, **to-chined** cracked, chapped.
265 **rowe** rough, unkempt.
266 **girdel-stede** i.e., waist.
272 **the soun gan shille** the sound shrilled, resounded.

That alle the wilde bestes that ther ben
For joye abouten him they teen;+
275 And alle the foweles that ther were
Come and sete on ech a brere+
To here his harpyng a-fyn—+
So muche melodye was ther-inne.
And whan he his harpyng lete wolde,
280 No beste by him abide nolde.

He myghte see him bisides,
Ofte in hot undren-tides,
The kyng of fairye wyth his route
Come to hunte him al aboute,+
285 Wyth dim cry and blowynge,
And houndes also wyth him berkynge.
But no beste they ne nome,
Ne nevere he niste+ whider they bicome.
And other while he myghte him see,+
290 As a greet ost+ by him tee,+
Wel atourned+ ten hundred knightes,
Ech i-armed to his rightes,+
Of countenaunce stout and fiers,+
Wyth many desplayed+ baners,
295 And ech his swerd i-drawen holde—

274 **teen** draw, approach.
276 **brere** twig, briar.
277 **a-fyn** to the end.
284 **aboute** i.e., all around him.
285 Harley MS. reads: *With dvnnyng & with blowyng*. Ashmole MS.
reads: *Wyth dynne, cry, & wyth blowyng*.
288 **Ne nevere he niste** He never knew.
289 **him see** see (for) himself.
290 **ost** host, army. **tee** go.
291 **atourned** equipped, accoutered.
292 **to his rightes** i.e., properly.
293 **countenaunce stout and fiers** strong and stout bearing.
294 **desplayed** unfurled.

But nevere he niste whider they wolde.
And other while he saw othre thyng:
Knightes and ladies come daunsyng
In queynte+ atire, gisely,+
300 Queynte pas+ and softely;
Tabours and trompes+ yede him by,
And al manere mynstralcye.
   And on a day he saw him biside
Sixty ladies on hors ride
305 Gentil and joly as brid on rys—+
Noght oon man amonges hem ther nis;
And ech a faucon+ on honde bar,
And riden on haukyng by a ryver.
Of game they founde wel good haunt,+
310 Mallardes, heroun, and cormeraunt.
The foweles of the water arise,
The faucons hem wel devise—+
Ech faucon his pray slough.
That saw Orfeo, and lough:+
315 "Parfay!" quod he, "ther is faire game.
Thider I wyl, by Goddes name!
I was y-won+ swich werk to see."
He aros and thider gan tee.+
To a lady he was i-come,

---

299 **queynte** elegant. **gisely** skillfully.
300 **Queynte pas** elegantly pace, step.
301 **Tabours and trompes** tabors and trumpets.
305 **joly as brid on rys** joyous as bird on spray.
307 **faucon** falcon.
307–308 The shift from singular to plural, like the frequent shifts of
    tense, is in the Auchinleck MS.
309 **wel good haunt** a great plenty.
312 **devise** descry, aim at.
314 **lough** laughed.
317 **y-won** accustomed.
318 **tee** approach.

320   Biheeld, and hath wel under-nome,+
       And seeth by alle thyng that it is
       His owene quene, Dame Heurodis.
       Yerne+ he biheeld hire, and she him eke,
       But nother to other a word ne spak.

325   For misese that she on him seigh,+
       That hadde ben so riche and so heighe,
       The teres felle out of hir eye.
       The othre ladies this y-seighe
       And maden hire awey to ride—

330   She moste wyth him no lenger abide.
       "Allas," quod he, "Now me is wo!
       Why nyl deeth now me slo?+
       Allas! Wrecche! that I ne myghte
       Deye now after this sight!

335   Allas! to longe lasteth my lyf
       Whan I ne dar noght wyth my wyf
       (Ne she to me) oon word speke.
       Allas! Why nyl myn herte breke?
       Parfay!" quod he, "Tide what bitide,+

340   Whider-so thise ladies ride,
       The selve+ weye I wyl strecche!+
       Of lyf ne deeth me ne recche!"+
       His sclavin+ he dide on also spak,+

---

320 **under-nome** recognized.

323 **Yerne** eagerly.

323–324 Harley MS. reads: *But þer myзt non with oþer speke / (þey [though] sche hym knewe & he hur eke).*

325 **seigh** = *saw.*

332 **slo** = *slee.*

333 *Wrecche* refers to himself.

339 **Tide what bitide** come what may.

341 **selve** same. **strecche** go.

342 **recche** reck, care. Either *me ne recceth* or *I me ne recche* would be normal here.

343 **sclavin** pilgrim's mantle. **also spak** straightway.

And heng his harpe upon his bak,
345 And hadde wel good wylle to gon;
He ne spared nother stub ne ston.⁺
In at a rokke⁺ the ladies rideth,⁺
And he after, and noght abideth.
Whan he was in the rokke i-go
350 Wel three myle other mo,
He cam into a faire contree
As bright so sonne on somers day,
Smothe and playn and al grene—
Hil ne dale nas ther non i-sene.

355 Amidde the lond a castel he seigh,
Riche and royal and wonder heighe;
Al the ute-moste⁺ wal
Was clere and shene as cristal;
An hundred toures ther were aboute
360 Degisely⁺ and batailed⁺ stoute;
The butras⁺ cam out of the diche⁺
Of reed gold i-arched riche;
The vousour⁺ was avowed⁺ al
Of ech manere diverse aumal.⁺

365 Wythinne ther were wide wones⁺
Al of precious stones;
The worst piler⁺ on to biholde
Was al of burnist gold.
Al that lond was evere light,

346 **ne spared nother stub ne ston** i.e., stopped for nothing.
347 **rokke** rock, cliff. **rideth** = *ride*.
357 **ute-moste** outermost.
360 **Degisely** wonderful. **batailed** crenelated.
361 **butras** buttress. **diche** moat.
363 **vousour** vaulting. **avowed** colored, adorned.
364 **aumal** enamel.
365 **wones** dwelling places.
367 **piler** pillar.

17

370   For whan it sholde be therk⁺ and nyght,
      The riche stones lighte gonne
      As bright as doth at noon the sonne.
      No man may telle, ne thenke in thoght,
      The riche werk that ther was wroght.

375   By alle thyng him think'th that it is
      The proude court of paradys!
      In this castel the ladies alight;
      He wolde in after, if he myghte.
         Orfeo knokketh at the yate.

380   The porter was redy ther-ate,
      And axed what he wolde have y-do.
      "Parfay!" quod he, "I am a mynstral, lo!
      To solace thy lord wyth my glee,
      If his swete wylle be."

385   The porter un-dide the yate anon
      And lett him into the castel gon.
         Than he gan biholde aboute al
      And saw lyinge wythinne the wal
      Of folk that were thider i-broght,

390   And thoght dede, and nere⁺ noght.
      Some stode wythouten heed,
      And some non armes nadde,⁺
      And some thurgh the body hadde wounde,
      And some laye wood,⁺ i-bounde,

395   And some armed on hors sete,
      And some a-strangled as they ete,
      And some were in water a-dreynt,⁺

---

370 **therk** dark.
390 **nere** = *ne were.* Harley MS. reads: *Al dede were þey nouȝt.*
392 **nadde** = *ne hadde.*
394 **wood** mad.
395–396 Ashmole MS. reads: *And som wer strangyld at þer mete, | And men þat were nomen wyth þem ete.*
397 **a-dreynt** drowned.

And some wyth fyr al for-shreynt;+
Wyves ther laye on child-bedde,
400 Some dede and some a-wedde.+
And wonder fele ther laye bisides
Right as they slepe her undren-tides.+
Ech was thus in this world i-nome,
Wyth fairye+ thider i-come.
405 Ther he saw his owene wyf,
Dame Heurodis, his leve lyf,
Slepe under an ympe-tree.
By hir clothes he knew that it was she.
    And whan he hadde biholde thise merveils alle,
410 He went into the kynges halle.
Than saw he ther a seemly sight—
A tabernacle+ blisful and bright.
Ther-inne her maister kyng sete,
And her quene, faire and swete;
415 Her crounes, her clothes shine so brighte,
That unethe biholde he hem myghte.
Whan he hadde biholde al that thyng,
He kneled adoun bifore the kyng:
"O Lord," he seyde, "if it thy wylle were,
420 My mynstralcye thou sholdest y-here."+
The kyng answerde: "What man artow+
That art hider i-comen now?
I, ne non that is wyth me,
Ne sente nevere after thee.
425 Sithen-that I heer regne+ gan

398 **for-shreynt** shriveled.
400 **a-wedde** gone mad.
402 **undren-tides** i.e., their midmorning naps.
404 **fairye** magic, enchantment.
412 **tabernacle** dais under a canopy.
420 **y-here** hear.
421 **artow** = *art thou.*
425 **regne** reign.

I ne fond nevere so fool-hardy man,
That thider to us durste wende
But that I him wolde of-sende."+
"Lord," quod he, "Trowe ful wel,
430   I nam+ but a poure mynstral,
And, Sire, it is the manere of us
To seche many a lordes hous;
Thogh we noght welcome ne be,
Yet we mote profre+ forth oure glee."
435   Bifore the kyng he sat adoun,
And took his harpe so myrie of soun,
And tempreth+ his harpe as he wel can;
And blisful notes he ther gan,
That alle that in the paleys were
440   Come to him for-to here,
And liggen+ adoun to his feet,
Hem thinketh his melodye so swete.
The kyng herkneth and sitt+ ful stille—
To here his glee he hath good wylle.
445   Good bourde+ he hadde of his glee;
The riche quene also hadde she.
Whan he hadde stynt his harpyng,
Than seyde to him the kyng:
"Mynstral, me liketh wel thy glee.
450   Now axe of me what+ it be;
Largely+ I wyl thee paye.
Now speek, and thou myghte assaye."+

428 **of-sende** send for.
430 **nam** = *ne am.*
434 **profre** offer.
437 **tempreth** tunes.
441 **liggen** lie.
443 **sitt** = *sitteth.*
445 **bourde** pleasure.
450 **what** i.e., whatsoever.
451 **Largely** generously.
452 **assaye** test, try (me).

"Sire," he seyde, "I biseche thee
That thou woldest yeve me
455 That ilke lady, bright on blee,+
That slepeth under the ympe-tree."
"Nay," quod the kyng, "that noght nere!
A sory couple of you it were!
For thou art lene, rowe,+ and blak,
460 And she is lufsom, wythouten lak.+
A lothly+ thyng it were, for-thy,
To seen hire in thy companye!"
    "O Sire," he seyde, "Gentil Kyng,
Yet were it a wel fouler thyng
465 To here a lesyng+ of thy mouthe:
So, Sire, as ye seyde nouthe,+
What I wolde axe, have I sholde—
And nedes thou most thy word holde."
The kyng seyde, "Sithen it is so,
470 Tak hire by the honde and go:
Of hire I wyl that thou be blithe!"
He kneled adoun and thonked him swithe;
His wyf he took by the honde
And did him swithe out of that londe,
475 And wente him out of that thede:+
Right as he cam, the weye he yede.+
So long he hath the weye i-nome,
To Winchester he is i-come,
That was his owene citee—
480 But no man knew that it was he.

455 **blee** complexion.
459 **rowe** rough, unkempt.
460 **lak** blemish.
461 **lothly** loathsome.
465 **lesyng** lie.
466 **nouthe** (just) now.
475 **thede** land, country.
476 **yede** went.

No forther thanne the tounes ende
For knoweleche⁺ ne durste he wende;
But wyth a beggar, y-bilt ful narwe,⁺
Ther he took his herbarwe⁺
485 (To him and to his owene wyf)
As a mynstral of poure lyf;
And axed tidynges of that lond,
And who the kyngdom held in hond.
The poure beggar in his cote⁺
490 Tolde him everich a grote:⁺
How her quene was stole aweye
Ten yere gon wyth fairye,
And how her kyng en⁺ exile yede—
But no man niste in which thede;
495 And how the styward the lond gan holde,
And othre many thynges him tolde.

A-morwe ayein⁺ none-tide
He made his wyf ther abide;
The beggars clothes he borwed anon
500 And heng his harpe his rigge⁺ upon,
And wente him into that citee,
That men myghte him biholde and see.
Erles and barouns bolde,
Burgeys⁺ and ladies him gonne biholde:

481–482 These lines, inconsistent with line 503 ff., are omitted in the
    other versions.
482 **knoweleche** for (fear of) recognition. *he* is supplied.
483 *y-bilt ful narwe* refers to the building in which Orfeo took lodging.
484 **herbarwe** = *herber* lodging.
489 **cote** cottage, mean dwelling.
490 **everich a grote** every bit.
493 **en** = *in*.
497 **ayein** toward.
500 **rigge** back.
504 **Burgeys** burgesses, citizens.

505   "Lo," they seyde, "swich a man!
     How longe the heer hongeth him upon!
     Lo, how his berd hongeth to his knee!
     He is i-clongen+ al-so a tree!"
     And as he yede in the strete,
510   Wyth his styward he gan mete,
     And loude he sette on him a cry:
     "Sire Styward," he seyde, "Mercy!
     I am an harpour of hethenesse.+
     Help me now in this distresse!"
515   The styward seyde, "Com wyth me, com!
     Of that I have thou shalt have som;
     Every good harpour is welcome me to
     For my lordes love, Sir Orfeo."
       In the castel the styward sat atte mete,
520   And many lordyng was by him sete;
     Ther were trompours and tabourers,+
     Harpours fele and crouders:+
     Muche melodye they maden alle.
     And Orfeo sat stille in the halle
525   And herkneth whan they ben al stille.
     He took his harpe and tempred shille.+
     The blisfullest notes he harped ther
     That evere any man y-herde wyth ere:
     Ech man liked wel his glee.
530   The styward biheeld and gan y-see,
     And knew the harpe al-so blive.+
     "Mynstral," he seyde, "so moot I thrive,+
     Wher haddest thou this harpe, and how?
     I preye that thou me telle now."

508 **i-clongen** withered, shriveled.
513 **hethenesse** foreign, pagan lands.
521 **trompours and tabourers** trumpeters and drummers.
522 **crouders** crwthplayers, fiddlers.
526 **shille** tuned shrilly.
531 **blive** quickly.
532 **so moot I thrive** as I may prosper.

535 "Lord," quod he, "in uncouth thede,+
Thurgh a wildernesse as I yede,
Ther I fond in a dale
Wyth leouns a man to-tore smale,
And wolves him frete+ wyth teeth so sharpe;
540 By him I fond this ilke harpe—
Wel ten yere it is a-go."
"O!" quod the styward, "Now me is wo!
That was my lord, Sir Orfeo!
Allas! Wrecche! what shal I do,
545 That have swich a lord i-lorn?
A, wei! that I was i-born—
That him was so hard grace i-yarked+
And so vile+ deeth i-marked!"
Adoun he fel a-swowne+ to grounde.
550 His barouns him toke up in that stounde+
And tellen him how it geth:+
"It nis no boot+ of mannes deeth."
   Kyng Orfeo knew wel by than
His styward was a trewe man
555 And loved him as he oghte to do;
And stondeth up and seyth thus, "Lo,
Styward, herkne now this thyng!
If I were Orfeo the kyng,
And hadde i-suffred ful yore
560 In wildernesse muchel sore,
And hadde i-wonne my quene aweye
Out of the londe of fairye,

535 **thede** land, country.
539 **frete** gnawed, devoured.
547 **i-yarked** appointed, ordained.
548 **vile** miserable.
549 **a-swowne** in a swoon.
550 **stounde** in that moment, thereupon.
551 **geth** = *goth* goes (inevitably).
552 **It nis no boot** there is no remedy.

And hadde i-broght the lady hende
Right heer to the tounes ende,
565 And wyth a beggar hire in i-nome
And were myself hider i-come,
Pourely to thee, thus stille,
For-to assaye thy gode wylle,
And I fond thee thus trewe,
570 Thou ne shold'st it nevere rewe:
Sikerly, for love or ay,+
Thou shold'st be kyng after my day.
And if thou of my deeth haddest ben blithe,
Thou shold'st have voided+ al-so swithe."
575 Tho alle tho that ther-inne sete,
That it was Kyng Orfeo underyete,+
And the styward him wel knew.
Over and over the bord+ he threw,
And fel adoun to his feet;
580 So dide everich lord that ther sete,
And alle they seyde at oon criyng:
"Ye beth oure lord, Sire, and oure kyng!"
Glade they were of his lyve!
To chambre they ladde him al-so blive,
585 And bathede him, and shavede his berd,
And tirede+ him as a kyng apert.+
And sithen, wyth greet processioun,
They broghte the quene into the toun,
Wyth al maner mynstralcye.
590 Lord! ther was greet melodye!
For joye they wepe wyth her eye
That hem so sound i-comen seighe.+

571 **for love or ay** for love or fear (i.e., in any event).
574 **voided** been banished.
576 **underyete** perceived, realized.
578 **bord** board, table.
586 **tirede** attired. **apert** for all to see.
592 **seighe** = *sawe*.

Now Kyng Orfeo newe crouned is,
And his quene, Dame Heurodis,
595 And lyvde longe after-ward;
And sithen was kyng the styward.

Harpours in Britayne after than
Herde how this merveil bigan,
And made heer-of a lay of good likyng+
600 And nemned+ it after the kyng.
That lay "Orfeo" is i-hote: +
Good is the lay, swete is the note.
Thus cam Sir Orfeo out of his care.
God graunte us alle wel to fare! Amen.

599 **good likyng** delight.
600 **nemned** named.
601 **i-hote** called.

The Cursed Dancers
of Colbek

Caroles, wrastlynges, other somer games—
Whoso evere haunteth[+] any swiche shames
In chirche other[+] in chirche-yeerd,
Of sacrilege he may be afeerd;
5   Or entreludes[+] or syngyng,
Or tabour[+] bete or other pipyng—
Alle swiche thyng forboden is
Whil the preest stondeth at messe.[+]
Alle swiche to every good preest is loth,
10 And sonner[+] wyl he make him wroth
Thanne he wyl that hath no wyt,
Ne understondeth not Holy Writ;
And specially at heighe tymes,
Caroles to synge and rede rymes[+]
15 Noght in none holy stedes[+]
That myghte destourbe the prestes bedes,[+]
Or if he were in orisoun
Or any other devocioun:
Sacrilege is al it tolde,
20 This and many other folde.
    But for-to leve[+] in chirche to daunce,
I shal you telle a ful greet chaunce,

2 **haunteth** frequents.
3 **other** or.
5 **entreludes** comic plays, farces.
6 **tabour** tabor.
8 **messe** mass.
10 **sonner** sooner.
14 **rymes** (trivial) poems.
15 **stedes** places.
16 **bedes** prayers.
21 **leve** leave off.

And I trowe, the moste that fel[+]
Is as sooth as the Gospel:
25 And fel this chaunce in this londe,
In Englond, as I understonde;
In a kynges tyme that highte[+] Edward
Fel this chaunce that was so hard.

It was upon a Christemasse nyght
30 That twelve foles[+] a carole dighte;[+]
In woodhede,[+] as it were in contek,[+]
They come to a toun man calleth Colbek.
The chirche of the toun that they to come
Is of Seint Magne that suffred martyrdom;
35 And of Seint Bukcestre it is also,
Seint Magnes suster, that they come to.
Her names of alle thus fond I write,
And as I wot now shullen ye wite:
Her lodes-man[+] that made hem glew,[+]
40 Thus is write, he highte Gerlew;
Two maydens were in her coveyne,[+]
Mayden Merswynde and Wybessyne.
Alle thise come thider for that enchesoun[+]
Of the prestes doghter of the toun.
45   The preest highte Robert, as I can ame;[+]
Azone highte his sone by name;
His doghter that thise wolde have,
Thus is write, that she highte Ave.

23 **fel** i.e., befell.
27 **highte** was called.
30 **foles** fools. **dighte** arranged.
31 **woodhede** madness. **contek** competition.
39 **lodes-man** leader. **glew** = *glee.*
41 **coveyne** band.
43 **for that enchesoun** i.e., for that reason, because.
45 **as I can ame** as I guess.

Echoon consented to oon wylle
50   Who sholde gon Ave out to tille.+
They graunted echoon out to sende
Bothe Wybessyne and Merswynde.
   Thise wommen yede+ and tollede+ hire oute
Wyth hem to carole the chirche aboute.
55   Bevune ordeyned her carolyng,
Gerlew endited+ what they sholde synge.
This is the carole that they songe,
As telleth the Latyn tonge:
      "Equitabat Beuo per siluam frondosam,
60   Ducebat secum Merswyndam formosam.
      Quid stamus? Cur non imus?"
      "By the leved+ wode rod Bevolyne,
Wyth him he ledde faire Merswyne.
Why stonde we? Why gon we noght?"
65   This is the carole that Grysly wroghte.
This song songe they in chirche-yeerd—
Of folye were they no thyng afeerd—
Unto the matynes were alle don
And the messe sholde bigynne soon.
70   The preest him revest+ to bigynne messe,
And they ne lefte ther-fore, nevere-the-lesse,
But daunsed forth as they bigonne—
For al the messe they ne blonne.+
   The preest that stood at the autere+

50 **tille** entice.
53 **yede** went. **tollede** enticed.
56 **endited** dictated, suggested.
62 **leved** leafy.
62–64 translates the Latin above.
70 **him revest** vested himself.
73 **blonne** ceased.
74 **autere** altar.

75 And herde her noise and her bere,+
    From the autere doun he nam+
    And to the chirche porche he cam,
    And seyde, "On Goddes half, I you forbidde
    That ye no lenger don swich dede;
80 But cometh inne on faire manere
    Goddes servise for-to here,
    And doth at Cristen mannes lawe—
    Caroleth no more, for Cristes awe!+
    Worshipeth him wyth al youre myght
85 That of the virgine was born this nyght!"
        For al his biddyng, lefte they noght,
    But daunsede forth, as they thoght.
    The preest ther-fore was sore agreved;
    He preyde God that he on bileved,
90 And for Seint Magne, that he wolde so werke
    (In whos worshipe set was the chirche)
    That swich a vengeaunce were on hem sent,
    Er they out of that stede were went,
    That they myghte evere right so wende
95 Unto that tyme twelve-month ende.
    (In Latyn that I fond thore,+
    He seyth not "twelve-month," but "evermore.")
    He cursed hem ther alsame+
    As they carolede on her game.
100 As soon as the preest hadde so spoke,
    Every hond in other so faste was loke+
    That no man myghte, wyth non wonder,
    That twelve-month parte hem asonder.
        The preest yede inne whan this was don

75 **bere** clamor.
76 **nam** took (his way).
83 **for Cristes awe** for fear of Christ.
96 **thore** = *ther*.
98 **alsame** together.
101 **loke** locked.

105 And comaunded his sone Azone
That he sholde gon swithe after Ave
Out of that carole algate⁺ to have.
But al to late that word was seyd,
For on hem alle was the vengeaunce leyd.
110   Azone wende wel for-to spede;
Unto the carole as-swithe⁺ he yede.
His suster by the arm he hente,
And the arm from the body wente.
Men wundrede alle, that ther wore,⁺
115 And merveil mowe ye here more;
For sith he hadde the arm in honde,
The body yede forth carolande;⁺
And neither body ne the arm
Bledde nevere blood, cold ne warm,
120 But was as drye wyth al the haunche⁺
As of the stok⁺ were riven⁺ a braunche.
   Azone to his fader went,
And broghte him a sory present.
"Loke, Fader," he seyde, "and have it heer,
125 The arme of thy doghter dere,
That was myn owene suster Ave
That I wende I myghte a save.
Thy cursyng now sene it is
Wyth vengeaunce on thyn owene flessh.
130 Felly⁺ thou cursedest and over-soon;
Thou axedest vengeaunce, thou hast thy boon."
You thar⁺ not axe if ther was wo

---

107 **algate** by all means.
111 **as-swithe** at once.
114 **wore** = *were*.
117 **carolande** = *carolynge*.
120 **haunche** i.e., shoulder.
121 **stok** stem. **riven** torn off.
130 **Felly** terribly.
132 **thar** need.

Wyth the preest and wyth many mo.
The preest that cursed for that daunce,
135 On som of his fel harde chaunce.
    He took his doghtres arm forlorn
And buryed it on the morn.
The nexte day the arm of Ave,
He fond it liggyng+ above the grave.
140 He buryed it on an other+ day,
And eft+ above the grave it lay.
The thridde tyme he buryed it,
And eft was it cast out of the pit.
The preest wolde burye it no more;
145 He dradde the vengeaunce ferly+ sore.
Into the chirche he bar the arm,
For drede and doute of more harm.
He ordeyned it for-to be
That+ every man myghte wyth eye it see.
150   Thise men that yede so carolande
Al that yere hond in honde,
They nevere out of that stede yede,
Ne non myghte hem thennes lede.
Ther the cursyng first bigan,
155 In that place aboute they ronne,
That nevere ne felte they no werynes+
As many bodies, for goyng+, dos;+
Ne mete ete, ne dronke drynke,
Ne slepte only alepy+ wynke.
160 Nyght ne day they wiste of non,

139 **liggyng** lying.
140 **an other** a second.
141 **eft** once more.
145 **ferly** wondrously.
149 **That** i.e., so that.
156 **werynes** weariness.
157 **for goyng** because of moving. **dos** = $do(n)$.
159 **alepy** (a) single.

32

Whan it was come, what it was gon;
Frost ne snow, hayl ne reyn,
Of cold ne hete felte they no peyne.
Heer ne nayles nevere grewe,
165 Ne solowede+ clothes ne turnede hewe;
Thonder ne lightnyng dide hem no dere+—
Goddes mercy dide hit from hem were+—
But songe that song that the wo wroghte:
"Why stonde we? Why gon we noght?"
170   What man sholde ther be in this lyve
That ne wolde it see and thider dryve?+
The Emperour Henry cam from Rome
For-to see this harde doom.+
What he hem saw he wepte sore
175 For the myschief that he saw thore.+
He dide come wrightes+ for-to make
Coveryng over hem, for tempeste sake.
But that they wroghte, it was in vayn,
For it cam to non+ certeyn;
180 For that they sette on oon day,
On the tother,+ doun it lay.
Ones, twyes, thries, thus they wroghte,
And al her makyng was for noght:
Myghte no coveryng hyle+ hem from colde
185 Til tyme of mercy that Crist hem wolde.
Tyme of grace fel thurgh His myght

---

165 **solowede** (were) soiled.
166 **dere** harm.
167 **were** ward off.
171 **dryve** hasten.
173 **harde doom** harsh fate.
175 **thore** = *ther*.
176 **wrightes** carpenters.
179 **cam to non** came to nothing.
181 **the tother** the second, next.
184 **hyle** protect.

At the twelve-monthe ende, on the Yole nyght.

. . . .

. . . .

190 That houre that he cursed hem inne,
That same houre they yede a-twynne.+
And as in twynklyng of oon eye
Into the chirche gonne they flye,
And on the pavement they felle alle doun
195 As they hadde ben dede, or falle in a swoun.
    Three dayes stille they laye echoon,
That non stired other flessh or bon;
And at the three dayes ende
To lyf God graunted hem to wende.
200 They sete up and speke apert+
To the parissh preest Sir Robert:
"Thou art ensaumple and enchesoun+
Of oure long confusioun.
Thou maker art of oure travail
205 That is to many greet merveil;
And thy travail shalt thou soon ende,
For to thy longe hom+ soon shalt thou wende."
    Alle they rise that ilke tide
But Ave—she lay deed biside.
210 Greet sorwe hadde hir fader, hir brother;
Merveil and drede hadde alle other.
I trowe no drede of soules deed,+

188–189 The lines read as follows: *þe same oure þat þe prest hem banned, / þe same oure atwynne þey woned.* The rhyme words are troublesome, and since the next two lines seem to be a rewriting of the couplet, lines 188 and 189 apparently should have been canceled.
191 **a-twynne** apart.
200 **apert** plainly.
202 **ensaumple and enchesoun** warning and cause.
207 **longe hom** eternal home.
212 **deed** death.

But wyth pyne⁺ was broght the body deed.⁺
The firste man was the fader, the preest,
215 That deyde after the doghter nest.⁺
This ilke arm that was of Ave,
That non myghte lay in grave,
The emperour dide a vessel werche⁺
To don it in and honge in the chirche,
220 That alle men myghte see it and knowe,
And thenke on the chaunce whan they it sawe.
    Thise men that hadde gon thus carolande,
Al the yeer, faste hond in honde,
Thogh that they were than asonder,
225 Yet al the world spak of hem wonder.
That same hoppyng that they first yede,
That daunce yede they thurgh lond and lede;⁺
And as they ne myghte first be unbounde,
So eft togidre myghte they nevere be founde;
230 Ne myghte they nevere come ageyn
Togidre to oon stede certeyn.
    Foure yede to the court of Rome
And evere hoppyng aboute they nome;⁺
Wyth sonder lepes⁺ come they thider,
235 But they come nevere eft togidre.
Her clothes ne roted, ne nayles grewe,
Ne heer ne wex, ne solowed⁺ hewe;
Ne nevere hadde they amendement⁺
That we herde, at any corseint,⁺

213 **pyne** suffering. **broght . . . deed** brought dead, i.e., died.
215 **nest** = *next*.
218 **dide a vessel werche** had a vessel made.
227 **thurgh lond and lede** i.e., throughout the world.
233 **nome** took (their way).
234 **sonder lepes** (?) / separate leaps.
237 **solowed** sullied.
238 **amendement** cure.
239 **corseint** shrine (of a saint).

240   But at the virgine Seint Edith,
       Ther he was botened,+ Seint Theodoric;
       On Oure Lady Day in Lenten-tide,
       As he slepte hir tombe biside,
       Ther he hadde his medicine+
245   At Seint Edith, the holy virgine.

       Brunyng, the bisshop of Seint Tolous,
       Wrot thise tales merveilous;
       Sith was his name of more renoun—
       Men callede him the Pope Leoun.
250   This at the court of Rome they wite,
       And in the cronicles it is write
       In many stedes beyonde the see
       More thanne is in this contree.
       Ther-fore men seye, and wel is trowed,
255   "The neer the chirche, the forther from God."
       So fare+ men heer by this tale,
       Som holde it but a trotevale;+
       In othre stedes it is ful dere
       And for greet merveil they wol it here.
260   A tale it is of faire shewyng,+
       Ensaumple and drede ayeins cursyng.
       This tale I tolde you to make you afeerd
       In chirche to carole, or in chirche-yeerd,
       Namely ayeins the prestes wylle:
265   Leveth, whan he biddeth you be stille.

241 **botened** given a remedy.
244 **medicine** cure.
256 **fare** regard.
257 **a trotevale** an idle story.
260 **of faire shewyng** i.e., that illustrates plainly.

Apollonius of Tyre

(From Gower's *Confessio Amantis*, Book VIII)

Of a cronique+ in dayes gon
The which is cleped+ Pantheon,
In loves cause I rede thus,
How that the grete Antiochus
5 (Of whom that Antioche took
His+ firste name, as seyth the book)
Was coupled to a noble quene,
And hadde a doghter hem bitwene.
But swich fortune cam to honde,
10 That deeth which no kyng may wythstonde,
But every lyf it moot obeye,
This worthy quene took aweye.
The kyng, which made muchel mone,+
Tho stood, as who seyth, al him one,+
15 Wythoute wyf, but natheles
His doghter, which was pereles+
Of beautee, dwelte aboute him stille.
But whan a man hath welthe at wylle,
The flessh is frele+ and falleth ofte;
20 And that this mayde tendre and softe,
Which in hir fadres chambres dwelte,
Wythinne a tyme wiste+ and felte:

1 **cronique** chronicle.
2 **cleped** called.
6 **His** i.e., its.
13 **mone** lamentation.
14 **him one** i.e., by himself.
16 **pereles** peerless, without equal.
19 **frele** frail.
22 **wiste** knew.

For likyng and concupiscence
Wythoute insight of conscience +
25   The fader so wyth lustes blente +
That he caste al his hol entente
His owene doghter for-to spille. +
This kyng hath leiser at his wylle
Wyth strengthe, and whan he tyme saw,
30   This yonge mayden he forlay; +
And she was tendre and ful of drede:
She coude noght hir maydenhede
Defende, and thus she hath forlorn
That flour which she hath longe born.
35   It helpeth noght althogh she wepe,
For they that sholde hir body kepe
Of wommen were absent as than.
And thus this mayden goth to man,
The wilde + fader thus devoureth
40   His owene flessh, which non socoureth, +
And that was cause of muchel care.
But after this unkynde fare +
Out of the chambre goth the kyng,
And she lay stille, and of this thyng
45   Wythinne hirself swich sorwe made,
Ther was non wight + that myghte hire gladde,
For fere of thilke + horrible vice.
Wyth that cam inne the norice +

24 **insight of conscience** sense of guilt.
25 **blente** blinded, deluded.
27 **spille** destroy, ruin.
30 **forlay** violated.
39 **wilde** unrestrained, powerful.
40 **socoureth** helps.
42 **unkynde fare** unnatural conduct.
46 **wight** person.
47 **thilke** = *the ilke* that same.
48 **norice** nurse.

Which from child-hod hire hadde kept,
50   And axeth if she hadde slept,
And why hir chere+ was unglad.
But she, which hath ben over-lad+
Of that which she myghte noght be wreke,+
For shame coude unethes+ speke;
55   And natheles mercy she preyde
Wyth wepynge eye, and thus she seyde:
"Allas, my suster! Weylawey,
That evere I saw this ilke day!
Thyng which my body first bigat
60   Into this world, only that
My worldes worshipe hath bireft."
Wyth that she swoneth now and eft
And evere wissheth after deeth,
So that wel-nigh hire lakketh+ breeth.
65   That other, which hir wordes herde,
In confortyng of hire answerde,
To lette+ hir fadres fool desire;
She wiste no recoverir:+
Whan thyng is don, ther is no boot,+
70   So suffren they that suffre mote;
Ther was non other which it wiste.
Thus hath this kyng al that him liste+
Of his likyng and his plesaunce,
And laste in swich continaunce,
75   And swich delit he took ther-inne

51 **chere** appearance.
52 **over-lad** overcome.
53 **wreke** revenged.
54 **unethes** not easily.
64 **hire lakketh** she lacked.
67 **lette** hinder, put off.
68 **recoverir** expedient.
69 **boot** remedy.
72 **al that him liste** all that he desires.

39

Him thoghte that it was no synne;
And she durste him no-thyng wythseye.+
   But fame, which goth every weye,
To sondry regnes,+ al aboute,
80 The grete beautee telleth oute
Of swich a mayde of heighe parage.+
So that for love of mariage
The worthy princes come and sende,
As they the whiche al honour wende,
85 And knewe no-thyng how it stood.
The fader, whan he understood
That they his doghter thus bisoghte,
Wyth al his wyt he caste and thoghte
How that he myghte fynde a lette;+
90 And swich a statut than he sette,
And in this wyse his lawe he taxeth,+
That what man his doghter axeth,
But if+ he coude his questioun
Assoile+ upon suggestioun
95 Of certeyn thynges that bifelle,
The whiche he wolde unto him telle,
He sholde in certeyn lese his heed.
And thus ther weren many deed,
Her hedes stondynge on the yate;+
100 Til atte laste, longe and late,
For lak of answere in the wyse,
The remenaunt+ that weren wyse
Escheweden to make assay.+

77 **wythseye** say in opposition.
79 **regnes** realms.
81 **parage** lineage.
89 **lette** hindrance.
91 **taxeth** ordains.
93 **But if** unless.
94 **Assoile** solve.
99 **yate** gate.
102 **remenaunt** remaining.
103 **Escheweden to make assay** i.e., avoided making the attempt.

Til it bifel upon a day
105 Appolinus the prince of Tyre—
Which hath to love a greet desire,
As he which in his heighe mood +
Was likynge + of his hote blood,
A yong, a fressh, a lusty knight —
110 As he lay musynge on a nyght
Of the tidynges whiche he herde,
He thoghte assaye how that it ferde. +
He was wyth worthy companye
Arrayed, and wyth good navye
115 To ship he goth; the wynd him dryveth,
And seyleth til that he arryveth +
Sauf in the port of Antioche.
He londeth, and goth to aproche
The kynges court and his presence.
120 Of every naturel science
Which any clerk + him coude teche
He coude + ynough, and in his speche
Of wordes he was eloquent;
And whan he saw the kyng present,
125 He preyeth he moot his doghter have.
The kyng ageyn bigan to crave, +
And tolde him the condicioun,
How first unto his questioun
He moot answere and fayle noght,
130 Or wyth his heed it shal ben boght:
And he him axeth what it was.

107 **mood** spirit, temper.
108 **likynge** finding pleasure in.
112 **how that it ferde** i.e., how things were.
116 **arryveth** comes to shore.
121 **clerk** scholar.
122 **coude** knew.
126 **crave** ask.

The kyng declareth him the cas,+
Wyth sterne look and sturdy+ chere
To him, and seyde in this manere:
135 "Wyth felonye I am upborn,
I ete and have it not forborn
My modres flessh, whos housebonde
My fader for-to seche I fonde,+
Which is the sone eke of my wyf.
140 Heer-of I am inquisitif;
And who that can my tale save,
Al quit+ he shal my doghter have;
Of his answere and if he fayle
He shal be deed wythoute faile.
145 For-thy, my sone," quod the kyng,
"Be wel avised of this thyng
Which hath thy lyf in jeupartie."+
Appolinus for his partie,+
Whan he this questioun hath herd,
150 Unto the kyng he hath answerd
And hath reherced oon and oon+
The poyntes, and seyde ther-upon:
"The questioun which thou hast spoke,
If thou wolt that it ben unloke,+
155 It toucheth al the privetee
Bitwene thyn owene child and thee,
And stant+ al hol upon you two."
The kyng was wonder sory tho,

132 **cas** circumstance, i.e., riddle.
133 **sturdy** resolute.
138 **fonde** try.
142 **Al quit** paid, i.e., freely, entirely.
147 **jeupartie** jeopardy.
148 **partie** part.
151 **oon and oon** one by one.
154 **unloke** unlocked, i.e., resolved.
157 **stant** = *stondeth*.

And thoghte, if that he seyde it oute,
160 Than were he shamed al aboute.
Wyth sleighe wordes and wyth felle+
He seyth, "My sone, I shal thee telle,
Thogh that thou be of litel wyt,
It is no greet merveil as yit:+
165 Thyn age may it noght suffise.
But loke wel thou noght despise
Thyn owene lyf, for of my grace
Of thritty dayes fulle a space
I graunte thee to ben avised."
170   And thus wyth leve and tyme assised+
This yonge prince forth he wente,
And understood wel what it mente:
Wythinne his herte as he was lered,+
That for-to maken him afered+
175 The kyng his tyme hath so delayed.
Wher-of he dradde and was esmayed+
Of tresoun that he deye sholde,
For he the kyng his sothe+ tolde.
And sodeynly, the nyghtes tide,
180 That more wolde he noght abide,
Al prively his barge he hente+
And home ageyn to Tyre he wente;
And in his owene wyt he seyde
For drede, if he the kyng biwreyde,+
185 He knew so wel the kynges herte,

161 **felle** deadly, cruel.
164 **yit** = *yet.*
170 **assised** appointed.
173 **lered** taught.
174 **afered** afraid.
176 **esmayed** dismayed, terrified.
178 **sothe** = *sooth* truth.
181 **hente** got, obtained.
184 **biwreyde** betrayed.

43

That deeth ne sholde he noght asterte,+
The kyng him wolde so pursewe.
But he, that wolde his deeth eschewe,+
And knew al this to-fore the hond,+
190 Forsake he thoghte his owene lond,
That ther wolde he noght abide;
For wel he knew that on som side
This tirant, of his felonye,
By som manere of trecherie
195 To greve his body wol not leve.
   For-thy wythoute take leve,
As prively as evere he myghte
He goth him to the see by nyghte
In shippes that be whete+ laden;
200 Her takel+ redy tho they maden
And hale+ up sayl and forth they fare.
But for-to tellen of the care
That they of Tyre bigonne tho,
Whan that they wiste he was a-go,
205 It is a pitee for-to here.
They losten lust, they losten chere,
They toke upon hem swich penaunce,
Ther was no song, ther was no daunce,
But every myrthe and melodye
210 To hem was than a maladye.
For un-lust+ of that aventure
Ther was no man which took tonsure;+
In dolful clothes they hem clothe.

186 **asterte** escape.
188 **eschewe** avoid, escape.
189 **to-fore the hond** beforehand.
199 **whete** (with) wheat.
200 **takel** gear.
201 **hale** pull, draw.
211 **un-lust** sorrow, disinclination.
212 **tonsure** cutting of hair.

The bathes and the stewes + bothe
215 They shette in by every weye.
Ther was no lyf which liste pleye
Ne take + of any joye kepe, +
But for her lige + lord to wepe.
And every wight seyde as he couthe,
220 "Allas, the lusty flour of youthe
Oure prince, oure heed, oure governour,
Thurgh whom we stoden in honour,
Wythoute the comun assent
Thus sodeynly is from us went!"
225 Swich was the clamour of hem alle.

But see we now what is bifalle
Upon the firste tale playn,
And turne we ther-to ageyn.
Antiochus the grete sire
230 Which ful of rancour and of ire
His herte bereth, so as ye herde,
Of that + this prince of Tyre answerde,
He hadde a feloun bacheler +
Which was his privy counseiler,
235 And Taliart by name he highte. +
The kyng a strong poyson him dighte +
Wythinne a boyste, + and gold ther-to;
In alle haste and bad him go
Streyt unto Tyre, and for no cost
240 Ne spare he til he hadde lost

214 **stewes** heated rooms used for vapor baths.
217 **take . . . kepe** takes heed.
218 **lige** liege.
232 **that** i.e., that which.
233 **feloun bacheler** wicked young knight.
235 **highte** was called.
236 **dighte** made ready.
237 **boyste** box.

45

The prince which he wolde spille.+
And whan the kyng hath seyd his wylle,
This Taliart in a galeye
Wyth alle haste he took his weye.
245   The wynd was good, he seyleth blive,
Til he took lond upon a ryve+
Of Tyre, and forth wyth al anon
Into the burgh he gan to gon,
And took his inn and bod a throwe.+
250   But for he wolde noght be knowe,
Disgysed than he goth him oute.
He saw the wepyng al aboute,
And axeth what the cause was,
And they him tolden al the cas,
255   How sodeynly the prince is go.
And whan he saw that it was so,
And that his labour was in vayn,
Anon he turneth hom ageyn;
And to the kyng, whan he cam nigh,
260   He tolde of that he herde and seigh,+
How that the prince of Tyre is fled;
So was he come ageyn unsped.+
The kyng was sory for a while,
But whan he saw that wyth no wyle
265   He myghte acheve his crueltee,
He stynte his wraththe and lett him be.

    But over this now for-to telle
Of aventures that bifelle
Unto this prince of whom I tolde,

241 **spille** destroy.
246 **ryve** shore.
249 **a throwe** a short while.
260 **seigh** = *saw*.
262 **unsped** not having succeeded.

270 He hath his right cours forth to holde
By ston and nedle,+ til he cam
To Tharse, and ther his lond he nam.
A burgeys riche of gold and fee+
Was thilke+ tyme in that citee,
275 Which cleped was Strangulio;
His wyf was Dionise also.
This yonge prince, as seyth the book,
Wyth hem his herbergage+ took.
And it bifel that citee so,
280 Bifore-tyme and than also,
Thurgh strong famyne which hem ladde+
Was non that any whete hadde.
Appolinus, whan that he herde
The myschief,+ how the citee ferde,
285 Al frely+ of his owene yifte+
His whete, among hem for-to shifte+
The which by ship he hadde broght,
He yaf, and took of hem right noght.
But sithen first this world bigan
290 Was nevere yet to swich a man
More joye mad thanne they him made:
For they were alle of him so glade,
That they for evere in remembraunce
Made a figure in resemblaunce
295 Of him, and in the comun place
They sette him up so that his face
Myghte every manere man biholde,

271 **ston and nedle** i.e., compass.
273 **fee** property, goods.
274 **thilke** = *the ilke* that same.
278 **herbergage** lodging.
281 **ladde** = *ledde*.
284 **myschief** distress.
285 **frely** very liberally. **yifte** gift.
286 **shifte** distribute.

So as the citee was biholde.
It was of latoun+ over-gilt:
300 Thus hath he noght his yifte spilte.+
    Upon a tyme wyth his route
This lord to pleye goth him oute,
And in his weye of Tyre he mette
A man, the which on knees him grette,
305 And Hellican by name he highte,
Which preyde his lord to have insighte
Upon himself, and seyde him thus,
How that the grete Antiochus
Awaiteth if he myghte him spille.
310 That other thoghte and heeld him stille,
And thonked him of his warnyng,
And bad him telle no tidyng,
Whan he to Tyre cam hom ageyn,
That he in Tharse him hadde seen.
315   Fortune hath evere ben muable+
And may no while stonde stable:
For now it heigheth, now it loweth,
Now stant upright, now over-throweth,
Now ful of blisse and now of bale,
320 As in the tellyng of my tale
Heer-afterward a man may lere,+
Which is greet routhe for-to here.

    This lord, which wolde don his beste,
Wythinne himself hath litel reste,
325 And thoghte he wolde his place chaunge
And seche a contree more straunge.
Of Tharsiens his leve anon

299 **latoun** latten, bronze.
300 **spilte** wasted.
315 **muable** mutable.
321 **lere** learn.

He took, and is to shippe gon.
His cours he nam, wyth sayl updrawe,
330 Wher-as Fortune doth the lawe,
And sheweth, as I shal reherce,
How she was to this lord diverse,
The which upon the see she ferketh.+
The wynd aros, the weder derketh,
335 It blewe and made swich tempeste
Non anker may the ship areste,
Which hath to-broken al his gere.
The shipmen stode in swich a fere,
Was non that myghte himself bistere,+
340 But evere awaite upon the lere+
Whan that they sholde drenche+ at ones.
Ther was ynough wythinne wones+
Of wepyng and of sorwe tho.
This yonge kyng mak'th muchel wo
345 So for-to see the ship travaile,
But al that myghte him noght avayle.
The mast to-brak, the sayl to-rof,+
The ship upon the wawes+ drof,+
Til that they sawe a londes coste.
350 Tho made avow the leste and moste,
Be so they myghten come a-londe;
But he which hath the see on honde,
Neptunus, wolde noght acorde;
But al to-breke cable and corde
355 Er they to londe myghte aproche;

333 **ferketh** conveys.
339 **bistere** bestir.
340 **lere** loss.
341 **drenche** drown.
342 **wones** possession.
347 **to-rof** was torn to pieces.
348 **wawes** waves. **drof** drove.

The ship to-clef+ upon a roche,+
And al goth doun into the depe.
But He that alle thyng may kepe
Unto this lord was merciable,
360 And broghte him sauf upon a table+
Which to the londe him hath upborn.
The remenaunt was al forlorn,
Wher-of he made muchel mone.
    Thus was this yonge lord him one,+
365 Al naked in a poure plit.+
His colour, which whilom was white,
Was than of water fade and pale,
And eke he was so sore a-cale+
That he wiste of himself no bote;+
370 It halp him no-thyng for-to mote+
To gete ageyn that he hath lorn.
But she which hath his deeth forborn,
Fortune, thogh she wol noght yelpe,+
Al sodeynly hath sent him helpe,
375 Whan him thoghte al grace aweye:
Ther cam a fisshere in the weye,
And saw a man ther naked stonde;
And whan that he hath understonde
The cause, he hath of him greet routhe,
380 And, only of his poure trouthe,+
Of swiche clothes as he hadde
Wyth greet pitee this lord he cladde.

356 **to-clef** split apart. **roche** rock.
360 **table** plank.
364 **one** alone.
365 **plit** plight.
368 **a-cale** a-cold.
369 **bote** = *boot* remedy.
370 **mote** wish.
373 **yelpe** boast.
380 **only of his poure trouthe** solely out of his humble honesty.

And he him thonked as he sholde,
And seyth him that it shal be yolde⁺

385 If evere he gete his stat⁺ ageyn;
And preyde that he wolde him seyn
If nigh were any toun for him.
He seyde, "Yee, Pentapolim,
Wher bothe kyng and quene dwellen."

390 Whan he this tale herde tellen,
He gladdeth him and gan biseche
That he the weye him wolde teche.
And he him taughte; and forth he wente
And preyde God wyth good entente

395 To sende him joye after his sorwe.
    It was noght passed yet mid-morwe
Whan thider-ward his weye he nam,
Wher soon upon the noon he cam.
He eet swich as he myghte gete,

400 And forth anon, whan he hadde ete,
He goth to see the toun aboute,
And cam ther as he fond a route
Of yonge lusty men wythalle.
And as it sholde tho bifalle,

405 That day was set of swich assise,⁺
That they sholde in the londes gise,⁺
As he herde of the peple seye,
Her comun game than to pleye;
And cried was that they sholde come

410 Unto the gamen alle and some
Of hem that ben delivere and wyhte⁺
To do swich maistrye as they myghte.

384 **yolde** repaid.
385 **stat** estate, position.
405 **assise** order, manner.
406 **gise** custom.
411 **delivere and wyhte** nimble and swift.

They made hem naked as they sholde,
For so that ilke game wolde,
415 As it was tho custume and us;+
Amonges hem was no refus.+
The flour of al the toun was there,+
And of the court also ther were.
And that was in a large place
420 Right evene afore+ the kynges face,
Which Artestrathes thanne+ highte;
The pleye was pleyde right in his sighte,
And who most worthy was of dede
Receive he sholde a certeyn mede+
425 And in the citee bere a pris.
     Appolinus, which war and wys+
Of every game couthe an ende,
He thoghte assaye, how so it wende,
And fel among hem into game;
430 And ther he wan him swich a name,
So as the kyng himself acounteth,
That he alle othre men surmounteth,
And bar the pris above hem alle.
The kyng bad that into his halle
435 At souper-tyme he shal be broght;
And he cam than and lefte it noght,+
Wythoute companye allone:
Was non so seemly of persone,
Of visage and of limes+ bothe,

415 **us** use, usage.
416 **refus** refused, rejected.
417 **there** = *ther.*
420 **Right evene afore** directly opposite.
421 **thanne** = *than* then.
424 **mede** reward.
426 **war and wys** i.e., skilled.
436 **lefte it noght** did not neglect it.
439 **limes** limbs.

440 If that he hadde what+ to clothe.
     At souper-tyme natheles,
     The kyng amiddes al the pres+
     Lett clepe him+ up among hem alle,
     And bad his mareshal+ of halle
445 To setten him in swich degree
     That he upon him myghte see.
     The kyng was sone+ set and served,
     And he, which hath the pris deserved
     After the kynges owene word,
450 Was made bigynne+ a myddel bord,+
     That bothe kyng and quene him seighe.
     He sat and caste aboute his eye
     And saw the lordes in estat,
     And wyth himself wex in debat
455 Thenkynge what he hadde lore;
     And swich a sorwe he took ther-fore,
     That he sat evere stille and thoghte,
     As he which of no mete roghte.+
     The kyng biheeld his hevynesse,+
460 And of his grete gentilesse
     His doghter, which was faire and good
     And atte bord bifore him stood,
     As it was thilke tyme usage,
     He bad to gon on his message
465 And fonde+ for-to make him glad.
     And she dide as hir fader bad,

---

440 **what** i.e., something (with which).
442 **pres** crowd, commotion.
443 **Lett clepe him** i.e., had him called.
444 **mareshal** = *marchal* marshal.
447 **sone** = *soon.*
450 **bigynne** i.e., to sit at the head of. **bord** table.
458 **roghte** recked, cared.
459 **hevynesse** sorrow.
465 **fonde** endeavor, try.

And goth to him the softe pas[+]
And axeth whennes and what he was,
And preyeth he sholde his thoghtes leve.
470 He seyth, "Madame, by youre leve,
My name is hote[+] Appolinus
And of my richesse it is thus—
Upon the see I have it lorn.[+]
The contree wher-as I was born,
475 Wher that my lond is and my rente,
I lefte at Tyre, whan that I wente:
The worshipe[+] of al this worldes aughte[+]
Unto the god ther I bitaughte."[+]
And thus togidre as they two speke
480 The teres ronne by his cheke.
The kyng, which ther-of took good kepe,[+]
Hath greet pitee to seen him wepe,
And for his doghter sente ageyn,
And preyde hire faire and gan to seyn
485 That she no lenger wolde drecche,[+]
But that she wolde anon forth fecche
Hir harpe and don al that she can
To gladde wyth that sory man.
And she to don hir fadres heste[+]
490 Hir harpe fette, and in the feste[+]
Upon a chaire which they fette
Hirself next to this man she sette;
Wyth harpe bothe and eke wyth mouthe

467 **the softe pas** (with) gentle step.
471 **hote** called.
473 **lorn** lost.
477 **worshipe** honor. **aughte** possession.
478 **bitaughte** delivered.
481 **kepe** heed, notice.
485 **drecche** torment, vex him.
489 **heste** behest, command.
490 **feste** (place of) feasting.

To him she dide al that she couthe
495 To make him chere—and evere he siketh+—
And she him axeth how him liketh.
"Madame, certes wel," he seyde,
"But if ye the mesure pleyde
Which, if you liste, I shal you lere,
500 It were a glad thyng for-to here."
"Ha, leve Sire," tho quod she,
"Now tak the harpe and lat me see
Of what mesure that ye mene."
Tho preyeth the kyng, tho preyeth the quene,
505 Forth wyth the lordes alle a-rewe,+
That he som myrthe wolde shewe.
He taketh the harpe and in his wyse
He tempreth,+ and of swich assise+
Syngynge he harpeth forth wythal,
510 That as a vois celestial
Hem thoghte it souneth in her ere,
As thogh that he an aungel were.
They gladden of his melodye,
But most of al the companye
515 The kynges doghter, which it herde,
And thoghte eke how he answerde
Whan that he was of hire opposed,+
Wythinne hir herte hath wel supposed
That he is of greet gentilesse.
520 His dedes ben ther-of witnesse
Forth wyth the wysdom of his lore;
It nedeth noght to seche more,
He myghte noght have swich manere,
Of gentil blood but if he were.

495 **siketh** sighs.
505 **a-rewe** in succession.
508 **tempreth** tunes. **assise** manner.
517 **opposed** questioned.

525 Whan he hath harped al his fille,
The kynges heste to fulfille,
Awey goth dissh, awey goth cuppe,
Doun goth the bord, the cloth was uppe;
They risen and gon out of halle.

530 The kyng his chamberleyn lett calle
And bad that he by alle weye
A chambre for his man purveye,
Which nigh his owne chambre be.
"It shal be don, my lord," quod he.
535 Appolinus of whom I mene
Tho took his leve of kyng and quene
And of the worthy mayde also,
Which preyde unto hir fader tho
That she myghte of that yonge man
540 Of tho sciences which he can+
His lore have; and in this wyse
The kyng hire graunteth his aprise,+
So that himself ther-to assente.
Thus was acorded er they wente
545 That he wyth al that evere he may
This yonge faire fresshe may+
Of that he couthe sholde enforme;
And ful assented in this forme
They toke leve as for that nyght.
550 And whan it was a-morwe light,
Unto this yonge man of Tyre
Of clothes and of good atire,
Wyth gold and silver to despende,
This worthy yonge lady sende;
555 And thus she made him wel at ese,

540 **can** knew.
542 **aprise** teaching.
546 **may** maiden.

And he wyth al that he can plese
Hire serveth wel and faire ageyn.
He taughte hire til she was certeyn
Of harpe, of citole,[+] and of rote,[+]
560   Wyth many a tun[+] and many a note
Upon musik, upon mesure,
And of hir harpe the temprure[+]
He taughte hire eke, as wel he couthe.
But as men seyn that frele is youthe,
565   Wyth leiser and continuaunce
This mayde fel upon a chaunce
That Love hath made him a querele
Ageyn hir youthe fresshe and frele,
That maugree wher[+] she wol or noght,
570   She moot wyth al hir hertes thoght
To Love and to his lawe obeye;
And that she shal ful sore abeye.[+]
For she wot nevere what it is,
But evere among she feleth this:
575   Thenkynge upon this man of Tyre
Hir herte is hot as any fyr,
And other while it is a-cale;[+]
Now is she reed,[+] now is she pale,
Right after the condicioun
580   Of hir ymaginacioun;
But evere among hir thoghtes alle,
She thoghte, what so may bifalle,
Or that she laughe, or that she wepe,

---

559 **citole, rote** stringed musical instruments.
560 **tun** tune.
562 **temprure** harmony.
569 **maugree wher** in spite of whether.
572 **abeye** pay, suffer.
577 **a-cale** a-cold.
578 **reed** red.

She wolde hir gode name kepe
585   For fere of wommanisshe shame.
But what in ernest and in game,
She stant for love in swich a plit
That she hath lost al appetit
Of mete, of drynke, of nyghtes reste,
590   As she that not+ what is the beste;
But for-to thenken al hir fille
She heeld hire ofte-tymes stille
Wythinne hir chambre, and goth noght oute;
The kyng was of hir lyf in doute,
595   Which wiste no-thyng what it mente.
    But fel a tyme, as he out wente
To walke, of princes sones three
Ther come and felle to his knee;
And ech of hem in sondry wyse
600   Bisoghte and profreth his servise
So that he myghte his doghter have.
The kyng, which wolde his honour save,
Seyth she is sik, and of that speche
Tho was no tyme to biseche;
605   But ech of hem do make a bille+
He bad, and write his owene wylle,
His name, his fader, and his good;+
And whan she wiste how it stood,
And hadde the billes overseen,
610   They sholden have answere ageyn.
Of this counseil they weren glad,
And writen as the kyng hem bad;
And every man his owene book
Into the kynges hond bitook.
615   And he it to his doghter sende,
And preyde hire for-to make an ende

590 **not** = *ne wot* knows not.
605 **bille** letter, writ.
607 **good** wealth.

And write ageyn hir owene hond,
Right as she in hir herte fond.
The billes weren wel received,
620 But she hath alle her loves weyved;+
And thoghte tho was tyme and space
To putte hire in hir fadres grace,
And wrot ageyn and thus she seyde:
"The shame which is in a mayde
625 Wyth speche dar noght ben unloke,+
But in writyng it may be spoke;
So write I to you, Fader, thus:
But if I have Appolinus,
Of al the world, what so bitide,
630 I wol non other man abide.
And certes, if I of him fayle,
I wot right wel wythoute faile
Ye shulle for me be doghterles."
This lettre cam, and ther was pres+
635 To-fore the kyng, ther as he stood;
And whan that he it understood,
He yaf hem answere by and by,
But that was don so prively,
That non of othres counseil+ wiste.
640 They toke her leve, and wher hem liste
They wente forth upon her weye.
      The kyng ne wolde noght biwreye+
The counseil for no manere heighe,+
But suffreth til he tyme seighe.+
645 And whan that he to chambre is come,

620 **weyved** put aside.
625 **unloke** unlocked, opened (up).
634 **pres** commotion, eagerness.
639 **counseil** (secret) counsel.
642 **biwreye** reveal.
643 **heighe** haste.
644 **seighe** might see.

He hath unto his counseil nome
This man of Tyre, and lett him see
The lettre and al the privette,
The which his doghter to him sente;

650 And he his knee to grounde bente
And thonketh him and hire also;
And er they wenten than a-two,+
Wyth good herte and wyth good corage+
Of ful love and ful mariage

655 The kyng and he ben hol acorded.+
And after, whan it was recorded
Unto his doghter how it stood,
The yifte of al this worldes good
Ne sholde have made hire half so blithe.

660 And forth wythal the kyng as swithe,
For he wol have hir good assent,
Hath for the quene hir moder sent.
The quene is come, and whan she herde
Of this matere how that it ferde,

665 She saw debat, she saw disese,
But if+ she wolde hir doghter displese,
And is ther-to assented ful.
Which is a dede wonderful,
For no man knew the sothe cas

670 But he himself, what man he was.
And natheles, so as hem thoghte,
His dedes to the sothe wroghte
That he was come of gentil blood:
Him lakketh noght but worldes good.

675 And as ther-of is no despeir,
For she shal ben hir fadres eyr,+

652 **a-two** apart.
653 **corage** spirit, disposition.
655 **hol acorded** fully agreed.
666 **But if** unless.
676 **eyr** heir.

And he was able to governe.
Thus wol they noght the love werne⁺
Of him and hire in non wyse,
680 But ther acorded they devise
The day and tyme of mariage.
Wher Love is lord of the corage⁺
Him thinketh longe er that he spede;
But atte laste unto the dede
685 The tyme is come, and in her wyse
Wyth greet offryng and sacrifise
They wedde and make a riche feste.
And every thyng which was honeste
Wythinnen hous and eke wythoute
690 It was so don, that al aboute
Of greet worshipe, of greet noblesse
Ther criede many a man largesse
Unto the lordes heighe and loude;
The knightes that ben yonge and proude,
695 They juste⁺ first and after daunce.
The day is gon, the nyghtes chaunce
Hath derked al the brighte sonne;
This lord, which hath his love wonne,
Is gon to bedde wyth his wyf,
700 Wher-as they ladde a lusty lyf;
And that was after somdel sene,
For as they pleyde hem bitwene,
They gete⁺ a child bitwene hem two,
To whom fel after muchel wo.

705 Now have I tolde of the spouseils.
But for-to speke of the merveils
Which afterward to hem bifelle,

678 **werne** refuse, turn aside.
682 **corage** heart.
695 **juste** joust.
703 **gete** begot.

61

It is a wonder for-to telle.
It fel a-day they riden oute,
710 The kyng and quene and al the route,
To pleyen hem upon the stronde, +
Wher-as they seen toward the londe
A ship seylynge of greet array. +
To knowe what it mene may,
715 Til it be come they abide;
Than seen they stonde on every side,
Endlonge+ the shippes bord to shewe,
Of penonceels+ a riche rewe. +
They axen whennes the ship is come:
720 From Tyre, anon answerde some;
And over this they seyden more
The cause why they comen fore
Was for-to seche and for-to fynde
Appolinus, which was of kynde
725 Her lige+ lord: and he appereth,
And of the tale which he hereth
He was right glad, for they him tolde
That for vengeaunce (as God it wolde)
Antiochus, as men may wite,
730 Wyth thonder and lightnyng is forsmite;
His doghter hath the same chaunce,
So be they bothe in oon balaunce.
"For-thy, oure lige lord, we seye
In name of al the lond, and preye,
735 That left al other thyng to don,
It like you+ to come soon

711 **stronde** seashore.
713 **greet array** great splendor.
717 **Endlonge** all along.
718 **penonceels** pennons. **rewe** row.
725 **lige** liege.
736 **It like you** may you be pleased.

And see youre owene lige men
Wyth othre that ben of youre ken,
That lyve in longyng and desire
740 Til ye ben come ageyn to Tyre."
This tale after the kyng it hadde
Pentapolim al over-spradde,
Ther was no joye for-to seche;
For every man it hadde in speche
745 And seyden alle of oon acord,
"A worthy kyng shal ben oure lord!
That+ thoghte us first an hevynesse
Is shape+ us now to greet gladnesse!"
Thus goth the tidyng over-al.
750   But nede he moot that nede shal:+
Appolinus his leve took,
To God and al the lond bitook+
Wyth al the peple long and brod,
That he no lenger ther abod.
755 The kyng and quene sorwe made,
But yet somdel they weren glade
Of swich thyng as they herden tho.
And thus bitwene the wele and wo
To ship he goth, his wyf wyth childe,
760 The which was evere meke and mylde
And wolde noght departe him fro,
Swich love was bitwene hem two.
Lichorida for hir office+
Was take, which was the norice,+
765 To wende wyth this yonge wyf,

747 **That** i.e., that which.
748 **shape** made, disposed.
750 **But nede he moot that nede shal** i.e., but he that shall need must
need.
752 **bitook** commended.
763 **office** service, employment.
764 **norice** nurse.

To whom was shape+ a woful lyf.
Wythinne a tyme, as it bitidde,
Whan they were in the see amidde,
Out of the north they sawe a cloude;
770 The storm aros, the wyndes loude
They blewen many a dredeful blast;
The welken+ was al over-cast,
The derke nyght the sonne hath under,
Ther was a greet tempeste of thonder;
775 The mone and eke the sterres bothe
In blake cloudes they hem clothe,
Wher-of her brighte look they hide.
This yonge lady wepte and cride,+
To whom no confort myghte avayle.
780 Of childe she bigan travaile,+
Wher she lay in a caban+ clos;+
Hir woful lord from hire aros,
And that was longe er any morwe,
So that in anguissh and in sorwe
785 She was delivered al by nyghte
And deed in every mannes sighte.
But natheles for al this wo
A mayde child was bore tho.
    Appolinus, whan he this knew
790 For sorwe a-swowne he overthrew,
That no man wiste in him no lyf.
And whan he wook, he seyde, "Ha, Wyf,
My lust, my joye, my desire,
My welthe and my recoverir,+

766 **shape** ordained, appointed.
772 **welken** welkin, sky.
778 **cride** = *criede.*
780 **travaile** labor.
781 **caban** cabin. **clos** secluded.
794 **recoverir** help.

795 Why shal I lyve, and thou shalt deye?
Ha, thou Fortune, I thee deffye,
Now hast thou don to me thy werste!+
Ha, herte, why ne wolt thou berste,
That forth wyth hire I myghte passe?
800 My peynes weren wel the lasse."
In swich wepyng and in swich cry
His dede wyf, which lay him by,
A thousand sithes+ he hire kiste;
Was nevere man that saw ne wiste
805 A sorwe unto his sorwe liche;+
For evere among upon the liche+
He fel swonynge, as he that soghte
His owene deeth, which he bisoghte
Unto the goddes alle above
810 Wyth many a piteous word of love:
But swiche wordes as tho were
Yet herde nevere mannes ere,
But only thilke+ which he seyde.
The maister shipman cam and preyde
815 Wyth othre swiche as be ther-inne,
And seyn that he may no-thyng wynne
Ageyn the deeth, but they him rede+
He be wel war and take hede,
The see by weye of his nature
820 Receive may no creature
Wythinne himself as for-to holde
The which is deed: for-thy they wolde
As they counseilen al aboute,

797 **werste** worst.
803 **sithes** times.
805 **liche** = *like.*
806 **liche** body, corpse.
813 **thilke** = *the ilke.*
817 **rede** advise.

65

The dede body casten oute:
825 For bettre it is, they seyden alle,
That it of hire so bifalle,
Thanne if they sholden alle spille.+
  The kyng, which understood her wylle
And knew her counseil that was trewe,
830 Bigan ageyn his sorwe newe
Wyth piteous herte, and thus to seye:
"It is al resoun that ye preye.
I am," quod he, "but oon allone,
So wolde I noght for my persone
835 Ther felle swich adversitee.
But whan it may no bettre be,
Doth than thus upon my word,
Lat make a cofre+ strong of bord
That it be ferme wyth leed and pich."+
840 Anon was made a cofre swich,
Al redy broght unto his hond;
And whan he saw and redy fond
This cofre made and wel enclowed,+
The dede body was bisowed+
845 In cloth of gold and leyde ther-inne.
And for he wolde unto hire wynne+
Upon som coste a sepulture,+
Under hir heed in aventure+

---

827 **spille** be destroyed. The sense of the preceding passage seems to
rest on the following reasoning: since the sea by nature casts a
dead body ashore, they must cast the body overboard lest the ship
be cast ashore with the body in it.
838 **cofre** coffer.
839 **leed and pich** lead and pitch.
843 **enclowed** nailed.
844 **bisowed** sewn.
846 **wynne** get, make.
847 **sepulture** tomb, sepulchre.
848 **in aventure** on a chance, i.e., just in case.

Of gold he leyde sommes grete
850 And of jeweles a strong beyete+
Forth wyth a lettre, and seyde thus:
"I, Kyng of Tyre Appolinus,
Do alle manere men to wite
That here and see this lettre write,
855 That helpeles wythoute reed+
Heer lieth a kynges doghter deed:
And who that happeth hire to fynde,
For charitee tak this in mynde,
And do so that she be bigrave+
860 Wyth this tresour, which he shal have."
Thus whan the lettre was ful spoke,
They have anon the cofre stoke+
And bounden it wyth iren faste,
That it may the wawes+ laste,
865 And stoppen it by swich a weye
That it shal be wythinne dreye,+
So that no water myghte it greve.
And thus in hope and good bileve
Of that the cors+ shal wel arryve,+
870 They caste it over bord as blive.+
    The ship forth on the wawes wente.
The prince hath chaunged his entente,
And seyth he wol noght come at Tyre
As thanne,+ but al his desire
875 Is first to seylen unto Tharse.

850 **strong beyete** i.e., a great amount.
855 ~~wythoute reed~~ i.e., unable to do anything.
859 **bigrave** buried.
862 **stoke** shut.
864 **wawes** waves, water.
866 **dreye** = *drye.*
869 **cors** corpse, body. **arryve** come to shore.
870 **as blive** immediately.
874 **thanne** = *than* then.

The wyndy storm bigan to skarse,+
The sonne ariseth, the weder clereth;
The shipman which bihynde stereth,
Whan that he saw the wyndes saughte,+
880 Towardes Tharse his cours he straughte.+

But now to my matere ageyn
To telle as olde bokes seyn,
This dede cors of which ye knowe
Wyth wynd and water was forthrowe
885 Now heer, now ther, til atte laste
At Ephesim the see upcaste
The cofre and al that was ther-inne.
Of greet merveile now bigynne
May here who that sitteth stille;
890 That God wol save may noght spille.+
Right as the cors was throwe a-londe,
Ther cam walkynge upon the stronde
A worthy clerk,+ a surgien,
And eke a greet phisician,
895 Of al that lond the wyseste oon,
Which highte Maister Cerymon;
Ther were of his disciples some.
This maister to the cofre is come;
He peiseth+ ther was somwhat in,
900 And bad hem bere it to his inn,
And goth himselve forth wythal.
    Al that shal falle, falle shal.
They comen hom and tarie noght;

876 **skarse** diminish.
879 **saughte** (become) at peace.
880 **straughte** directed.
890 **That God wol save may noght spille** that which God will save may
    not (come to) ruin.
893 **clerk** scholar.
899 **peiseth** i.e., felt by weighing.

68

This cofre is into chambre broght,
905 Which that they fynde faste stoke,+
But they wyth craft it have unloke.
They loken in, wher-as they founde
A body deed, which was biwounde
In cloth of gold, as I seyde er;
910 The tresour eke they founden ther
Forth wyth the lettre, which they rede.
And tho they token bettre hede;
Unsowed was the body soon,
And he, which knew what is to don,
915 This noble clerk, wyth alle haste
Bigan the veynes for-to taste,+
And saw hir age was of youthe,
And wyth the craftes which he couthe+
He soghte and fond a signe of lyf.
920 Wyth that this worthy kynges wyf
Honestely+ they token oute,
And maden fyres al aboute;
They leyde hire on a couche softe,
And wyth a shete+ warmed ofte
925 Hir colde brest bigan to hete,
Hir herte also to flakke+ and bete.
This maister hath hir every joynt
Wyth certeyn oyle and balsme enoynt,
And putte a licour in hir mouth,
930 Which is to fewe clerkes couth,
So that she covereth+ atte laste.
And first hir eyen up she caste,

905 **stoke** shut.
916 **taste** try, test.
918 **couthe** knew.
921 **Honestely** honorably.
924 **shete** sheet.
926 **flakke** flutter.
931 **covereth** recovers.

And whan she more of strengthe caughte,
Hir armes bothe forth she straughte,+
935 Heeld up hir hond and piteously
She spak and seyde, "Ha, wher am I?
Wher is my lord? What world is this?"
As she that wot noght how it is.
But Cerymon the worthy leche+
940 Answerde anon upon hir speche
And seyth, "Madame, ye ben here+
Wher ye be sauf, as ye shal here
Heer-afterward; for-thy as now
My counseil is, conforteth you:
945 For trusteth wel wythoute faile
There is no-thyng which shal you fayle
That oghte of resoun to be do."
Thus passen they a day or two;
They speke of noght as for an ende+
950 Til she bigan somdel amende
And wiste hirselve what she mente.
   Tho for-to knowe hir hol entente
This maister axeth al the cas,
How she cam ther and what she was.
955 "How I cam here,+ wot I noght,"
Quod she, "but wel I am bithoght
Of othre thynges al aboute."
From poynt to poynt and tolde him oute
As ferforthly+ as she it wiste.
960 And he hire tolde how in a kiste+
The see hire threw upon the lond,
And what tresour wyth hire he fond,

934 **straughte** stretched.
939 **leche** physician.
941 **here** = *heer* here.
949 **as for an ende** in short.
955 **here** = *heer* here.
959 **ferforthly** completely.
960 **kiste** chest.

Which was al redy at hir wylle,
As he that shoop⁺ him to fulfille
965 Wyth al his myght what thyng he sholde.
She thonketh him that he so wolde,
And al hir herte she discloseth,
And seyth him wel that she supposeth
Hir lord be dreynt,⁺ hir child also;
970 So saw she noght but alle wo.
Wher-of as to the world namore
Ne wol she turne, and preyeth ther-fore
That in som temple of the citee
To kepe and holde hir chastitee,
975 She myghte among the wommen dwelle.
Whan he this tale hire herde telle,
He was right glad, and made hire knowen
That he a doghter of his owene
Hath, which he wol unto hire yive⁺
980 To serve, whil they bothe lyve,
In stede of that which she hath lost;
Al only at his owene cost
She shal be rendred forth wyth⁺ hire.
She seyth, "Grant-mercy, leve Sire,
985 God quite⁺ it you, ther I ne may."
And thus they dryve forth⁺ the day
Til tyme cam that she was hol;
And tho they take her counseil hol,
To shape upon good ordinaunce⁺
990 And make a worthy purveiaunce⁺
Ayeins the day whan they be veyled.

964 **shoop** prepared.
969 **dreynt** drowned.
979 **yive** = *yeve.*
983 **rendred forth wyth** delivered to.
985 **quite** repay, reward.
986 **dryve forth** i.e., spend.
989 **ordinaunce** arrangement.
990 **purveiaunce** provision.

And thus, whan that they be counseiled,
In blake clothes they hem clothe,
This lady and the doghter bothe,
995 And yolde+ hem to religioun.
The feste and the professioun
After the reule of that degree
Was made wyth greet solempnitee
Wher-as Diane is seintefied.
1000 Thus stant this lady justefied
In ordre wher she thenketh to dwelle.

But now ageynward for-to telle
In what plit that hir lord stood inne.
He seyleth til that he may wynne
1005 The havene of Tharse, as I seyde er;
And whan he was arryved ther,
And it was thurgh the citee knowe,
Men myghte see wythinne a throwe+
As who seyth, al the toun at ones,
1010 That come ayeins+ him for the nones
To yeven him the reverence,
So glad they were of his presence;
And thogh he were in his corage+
Disesed,+ yet wyth glad visage
1015 He made hem chere, and to his inn,
Wher he whilom sojourned in,
He goth him streyte and was received.
And whan the pres of peple is weyved+
He taketh his hoste unto him tho,

995 **yolde** yielded, gave.
1008 **throwe** short time.
1010 **ayeins** toward.
1013 **corage** heart.
1014 **Disesed** dis-eased, troubled.
1018 **weyved** put aside, vacated.

1020 And seyth, "My freend Strangulio,
Lo, thus and thus it is bifalle,
And thou thyself art oon of alle,
Forth wyth thy wyf, whiche I most triste.+
For-thy, if that you bothe liste,
1025 My doghter Thaise by youre leve
I thenke+ shal wyth you bileve+
As for a tyme; and thus I preye
That she be kept by alle weye,
And whan she hath of age more
1030 That she be set to bokes lore.
And this avow to God I make,
That I shall nevere for hir sake
My berd for no likyng shave,
Til it bifalle that I have
1035 In covenable+ tyme of age
Biset hire unto mariage."
Thus they acorde, and al is wel,
And for-to resten him somdel,
As for a while he ther sojourneth;
1040 And than he taketh his leve and turneth
To shippe, and goth him hom to Tyre,
Wher every man wyth greet desire
Awaiteth upon his comynge.
But whan the ship cam in seylynge,
1045 And they perceiven it is he,
Was nevere yet in no citee
Swich joye mad as they tho made;
His herte also bigan to gladde
Of that he saw the peple glad.
1050 Lo, thus Fortune his hap hath lad:
In sondry wyse he was travailed,

1023 triste = *truste*.
1026 **thenke** intend. **bileve** remain.
1035 **convenable** suitable.

But how so evere he be assailed,
His lattere ende shal be good.

And for-to speke how that it stood
1055 Of Thaise his doghter, wher she dwelleth,
In Tharse, as the cronique telleth,
She was wel kept, she was wel loked,+
She was wel taught, she was wel boked,
So wel she spedde+ hire in hir youthe
1060 That she of every wysdom couthe,
That for-to seche in every lond
So wys an other no man fond,
Ne so wel taught at mannes eye.+
But wo worthe evere+ fals envye!
1065 For it bifel that tyme so,
A doghter hath Strangulio,
The which was cleped Philotenne:
But fame,+ which wol evere renne,
Cam alday+ to hir modres ere
1070 And seyth, wher evere hir doghter were
Wyth Thaise set in any place,
The comun vois, the comun grace
Was al upon that other mayde,
And of hir doghter no man seyde.+
1075 Who wroth+ but Dionise than?
Hir thoghte a thousand yere til whan
She myghte ben of Thaise wreke+

1057 **loked** i.e., looked after.
1059 **spedde** advanced.
1063 **at mannes eye** in the eyes of men.
1064 **wo worthe evere** i.e., may it ever go ill with respect to.
1068 **fame** i.e., rumor, reputation.
1069 **alday** continually.
1074 **seyde** i.e., said anything.
1075 **wroth** became angry.
1077 **wreke** avenged.

Of that she herde folk so speke.
And fel that ilke same tide
1080 That deed was trewe Lychoride
Which hadde ben servaunt to Thaise,
So that she was the worse at aise,+
For she hath thanne+ no servise
But only thurgh this Dionise
1085 Which was hir deedly enemy
Thurgh pure+ tresoun and envye.
She, that of al sorwe can,
Tho spak unto hir bondeman
Which cleped was Theophilus,
1090 And made him swere in counseil thus,
That he swich tyme as she him sette
Shal come Thaise for-to fette+
And lede hire out of alle sighte,
Wher-as no man hire helpe myghte,
1095 Upon the stronde nigh the see,
And ther he shal this mayden slee.
This cherles+ herte is in a traunce,
As he which dradde him of vengeaunce,
Whan tyme cometh an other day;
1100 But yet durste he noght seye nay,
But swor and seyde he shal fulfille
Hir hestes+ at hir owene wylle.
      The tresoun and the tyme is shape,+
So fel it that this cherles knape+
1105 Hath led this mayden ther he wolde

1082 **aise** = *ese* ease.
1083 **thanne** = *than* then.
1086 **pure** utter.
1092 **fette** = *fecche* fetch.
1097 **cherles** slave's, man's.
1102 **hestes** behests, commands.
1103 **shape** ordained.
1104 **knape** fellow.

Upon the stronde, and what she sholde
She was adrede; and he out-breyde+
A rusty swerd and to hire seyde,
"Thou shalt be deed." "Allas!" quod she,
1110 "Why shal I so?" "Lo thus," quod he,
"My lady Dionise hath bede+
Thou shalt be mordred in this stede."
This mayden tho for fere shrighte,+
And for the love of God Almyghte
1115 She preyeth that for a litel stounde+
She myghte knele upon the grounde
Toward the hevene for-to crave+
Hir woful soule if she may save.
And wyth this noise and wyth this cry,
1120 Out of a barge+ faste by
Which hidd was ther on scumerfare,+
Men sterten out and were ware
Of this feloun,+ and he to go,
And she bigan to crie tho,
1125 "Ha, mercy, help for Goddes sake!"
Into the barge they hire take,
As theves sholde, and forth they wente.
Upon the see the wynd hem hente,+
And maugree wher+ they wolde or non,
1130 To-fore the weder forth they gon;

1107 **out-breyde** (quickly) drew out.
1111 **bede** bidden.
1113 **shrighte** shrieked.
1115 **stounde** space of time.
1117 **crave** plead, ask.
1120 **barge** ship.
1121 **scumerfare** piracy.
1123 **feloun** cruel, wicked (person).
1128 **hente** seized.
1129 **maugree wher** in spite of whether.

76

Ther halp no sayl, ther halp non ore:+
Forstormed and forblowen sore
In greet peril so forth they dryve,
Til atte laste they arryve
1135 At Mitelene the citee.
In havene sauf and whan they be,
The maister shipman made him boun+
And goth him out into the toun,
And profreth Thaise for-to selle.
1140 Oon Leonin it herde telle,
Which maister of the bordel+ was,
And bad him gon a redy pas+
To fecchen hire; and forth he wente
And Thaise out of his barge he hente,
1145 And to this bordiller hire solde.
And he, that by hir body wolde
Take avantage, lett do crie+
That what man wolde his lechery
Attempte upon hir maydenhede,
1150 Ley doun the gold and he shal spede.
And thus whan he hath cried it oute
In sight of al the peple aboute,
He ledde hire to the bordel tho.
No wonder is thogh she be wo:
1155 Clos in a chambre by hirselve,
Ech after other ten or twelve
Of yonge men to hire in wente;
But swich a grace God hir sente,
That for the sorwe which she made

1131 **ore** oar.
1137 **boun** ready.
1141 **bordel** brothel.
1142 **a redy pace** at a quick footpace.
1147 **lett do crie** had announcement made.

1160 Was non of hem which power hadde
        To don hire any vilanye.
        This Leonin lett evere espye,+
        And waiteth after greet beyete;+
        But al for noght, she was forlete,+
1165 That mo men wolde ther noght come.
        Whan he ther-of hath hede nome+
        And knew that she was yet a mayde,
        Unto his owene man he seyde
        That he wyth strengthe ayeins hir leve
1170 Tho sholde hir maydenhod bireve.
        This man goth in, but so it ferde,
        Whan he hir woful pleyntes herde
        And he ther-of hath take kepe,+
        Him liste bettre for-to wepe
1175 Thanne don oght elles to the game.
        And thus she kepte hirself from shame,
        And kneleth doun to th'erthe and preyde
        Unto this man, and thus she seyde:
        "If so be that thy maister wolde
1180 That I his gold encrese sholde,
        It may noght falle by this weye.
        But suffre me to go my weye
        Out of this hous wher I am inne,
        And I shal make him for-to wynne
1185 In som place elles of the toun,
        Be so it be+ religioun,
        Wher that honeste wommen dwelle.
        And thus thou myghte thy maister telle,

1162 **lett evere espye** i.e., had (her) continually spied on.
1163 **beyete** gain.
1164 **forlete** left entirely alone.
1166 **hede nome** taken heed.
1173 **take kepe** taken heed.
1186 **Be so it be** i.e., just so it be.

That whan I have a chambre ther,
1190   Lat him do crie ay wide-wher,+
What lord that hath his doghter dere
And is in wyl that she shal lere
Of swich a scole+ that is trewe,
I shal hire teche of thynges newe,
1195   Which as non other womman can
In al this lond." And tho this man
Hir tale hath herd, he goth ageyn,
And tolde unto his maister playn
That she hath seyd; and ther-upon,
1200   Whan than he saw beyete non
At the bordel by cause of hire,
He bad his man to gon and spire+
A place wher she myghte abide,
That he may wynne upon som side
1205   By that+ she can: but atte leste
Thus was she sauf from this tempeste.
    He hath hire from the bordel take,
But that was noght for Goddes sake,
But for the lucre,+ as she him tolde.
1210   Now comen tho that comen wolde
Of wommen in her lusty youthe,
To here and see what thyng she couthe.
She can the wysdom of a clerk,
She can of every lusty werk
1215   Which to a gentil womman longeth,
And some of hem she underfongeth+
To the citole and to the harpe,

1190 **wide-wher** far and wide.
1193 **scole** school.
1202 **spire** inquire (for).
1205 **By that** i.e., by whatever (means).
1209 **lucre** money, gain.
1216 **underfongeth** receives, accepts (as students).

And whom it liketh for-to carpe+
Proverbes and demaundes sleighe;+
1220 An other swich they nevere seighe+
Which that science+ so wel taughte;
Wher-of she grete yiftes caughte,
That she to Leonin hath wonne.
And thus hir name is so bigonne+
1225 Of sondry thynges that she techeth,
That al the lond unto hire secheth
Of yonge wommen for-to lere.

Now lete we this mayden here+
And speke of Dionise ageyn
1230 And of Theophile the vileyn,
Of whiche I spak of now to-fore.
Whan Thaise sholde have ben forlore,
This false cherl to his lady
Whan he cam hom, al prively
1235 He seyth, "Madame, slayn I have
This mayde Thaise, and is bigrave
In privy place, as ye me bede.+
For-thy, Madame, taketh hede
And keep counseil, how so it stonde."
1240 This feend, which this hath understonde,
Was glad, and weneth+ it be sooth.
Now herkne heer-after how she doth.

1218 **carpe** utter, converse in.
1219 **demaundes sleighe** cunning questions.
1220 **seighe** = *sawe.*
1221 **science** knowledge.
1224 **bigonne** i.e., gone about, become known.
1228 **here** = *heer* here.
1237 **bede** bade.
1241 **weneth** supposes.

She wepeth, she sorweth, she compleyneth,
And of siknesse which she feyneth+
1245 She seyth that Thaise sodeynly
By nyghte is deed "as she and I
Togidre laye nigh my lord."
She was a womman of record,+
And al is leved+ that she seyth;
1250 And for-to yeve a more feith,
Hir housebonde and eke she bothe
In blake clothes they hem clothe,
And made a greet enterrement;+
And for the peple shal be blent,+
1255 Of Thaise as for the remembraunce,
After the royal olde usaunce+
A tombe of latoun+ noble and riche
Wyth an ymage unto hire liche+
Lyggynge+ above ther-upon
1260 They made and sette it up anon.
Hir epitaffe of good assise+
Was write aboute, and in this wyse
It spak: "O ye that this biholde,
Lo, heer lieth she, the which was holde
1265 The faireste and the flour of alle,
Whos name Thaisis men calle.
The Kyng of Tyre Appolinus

1244 **feyneth** feigns, pretends.
1248 **of record** of (good) report, repute.
1249 **leved** believed.
1253 **enterrement** interment.
1254 **blent** deluded.
1256 **usaunce** custom.
1257 **latoun** latten, bronze.
1258 **liche** = *like*.
1259 **Lyggynge** lying.
1261 **assise** order.

Hir fader was: now lieth she thus.
Fourtene yere she was of age
1270 Whan deeth hire took to his viage."+

Thus was this false tresoun hidd,
Which afterward was wide kidd,+
As by the tale a man shal here.
But for-to clare+ my matere,
1275 To Tyre I thenke to turne ageyn,
And telle as the croniques seyn.
Whan that the kyng was comen hom,
And hath left in the salte fom
His wyf, which he may noght foryete,
1280 For he som confort wolde gete,
He lett sumoune a parlement
To which the lordes were a-sent;+
And of the tyme he hath ben oute,
He seeth the thynges al aboute,
1285 And tolde hem eke how he hath fare
Whil he was out of londe fare;
And preyde hem alle to abide,
For he wolde at the same tide
Do shape for his wyves mynde,+
1290 As he that wol noght ben unkynde.
Solempne was that ilke office,
And riche was the sacrifise,
The feste royaly was holde;
And ther-to was he wel biholde:
1295 For swich a wyf as he hadde oon
In thilke dayes was ther non.

1270 **viage** voyage, journey.
1272 **kidd** known.
1274 **clare** declare.
1282 **a-sent** sent for.
1289 **mynde** memory.

Whan this was don, than he him thoghte
Upon his doghter, and bisoghte
Swiche of his lordes as he wolde,
1300 That they wyth him to Tharse sholde+
To fecche his doghter Thaise there:
And they anon al redy were.
To ship they gon and forth they wente
Til they the havene of Tharse hente.
1305 They londe and fayle of that they seche
By coverture+ and sleighte of speche.+
This false man Strangulio,
And Dionise his wyf also,
That he+ the bettre trowe myghte,
1310 They ladden him to have a sighte
Wher that hir tombe was arrayed.
The lasse yet he was myspayed,+
And natheles, so as he dorste,+
He curseth and seyth al the worste
1315 Unto Fortune, as to the blynde,
Which can no siker+ weye fynde;
For she him neweth evere among,
And medleth+ sorwe wyth his song.
But sith it may no bettre be,
1320 He thonketh God and forth goth he
Seylynge toward Tyre ageyn.
But sodeynly the wynd and reyn
Bigonne upon the see debate,
So that he suffre moot algate+

1300 **sholde** i.e., should go.
1306 **coverture** disguise. **sleighte** skill, trickery.
1309 **he** i.e., Appolinus.
1312 **myspayed** displeased.
1313 **dorste** = *durste* dared.
1316 **siker** safe, sure.
1318 **medleth** mingles.
1324 **algate** in any event.

1325 The lawe which Neptune ordeyneth;
Wher-of ful ofte tyme he pleyneth,+
And heeld him wel the more esmayed+
Of that he hath to-fore assayed.
So that for pure sorwe and care
1330 Of that he seeth his world so fare,
The reste he lefte of his caban,
That for the counseil of no man
Ageyn ther-inne he nolde come,
But hath benethe his place nome
1335 Wher he wepynge allone lay
Ther as he saw no light of day.
And thus to-fore the wynd they dryve,
Til longe and late they arryve
Wyth greet distresse, as it was sene,
1340 Upon this toun of Mitelene,
Which was a noble citee tho.
And hapneth thilke tyme so,
The lordes bothe and the comune
The heighe festes of Neptune
1345 Upon the stronde at the rivage,+
As it was custume and usage,
Solempneliche they biseighe.+
    Whan they this straunge vessel seighe
Come in, and hath his sayl avaled,+
1350 The toun ther-of hath spoke and taled.+
The lord which of the citee was,
Whos name is Athenagoras,
Was ther, and seyde he wolde see

1326 **pleyneth** laments, complains.
1327 **esmayed** dismayed.
1345 **rivage** landing place.
1347 **Solempneliche . . . biseighe** solemnly attended to.
1349 **avaled** let down.
1350 **taled** told (tales).

What ship it is, and who they be
1355 That ben ther-inne; and after soon,
Whan that he saw it was to don,
His barge was for him arrayed
And he goth forth and hath assayed.
He fond the ship of greet array,
1360 But what thyng it amounte+ may,
He seeth they maden hevy chere,
But wel him thinketh by the manere
That they be worthy men of blood,
And axeth of hem how it stood.
1365 And they him tellen al the cas,
How that her lord fordryve+ was,
And what a sorwe that he made,
Of which ther may no man him glade.
He preyeth that he her lord may see,
1370 But they him tolde it may noght be,
For he lieth in so derke a place,
That ther may no wight seen his face.
But for al that, thogh hem be loth,
He fond the laddre and doun he goth,
1375 And to him spak, but non answere
Ageyn of him ne myghte he bere
For oght that he can don or seyn;
And thus he goth him up ageyn.
Tho was ther spoke in many wyse
1380 Amonges hem that weren wyse,
Now this, now that, but atte laste
The wysdom of the toun this caste,+
That the yonge Thaise were a-sent.
For if ther be amendement
1385 To gladde wyth this woful kyng,

1360 **amounte** amount to, mean.
1366 **fordryve** driven about.
1382 **caste** proposed.

85

She can so muche of every thyng,
That she shal gladden him anon.
A messager for hire is gon,
And she cam wyth hir harpe on honde,
1390 And seyde hem that she wolde fonde
By alle weyes that she can
To gladde wyth this sory man;
But what he was she wiste noght.
But al the ship hire hath bisoght
1395 That she hir wyt on him despende,
In aunter if+ he myghte amende,
And seyn it shal be wel aquit.+
Whan she hath understonden it,
She goth hire doun, ther as he lay,
1400 Wher that she harpeth many a lay
And like an aungel sang wythal;
But he namore thanne the wal
Took hede of any thyng he herde.
And whan she saw that he so ferde,
1405 She falleth wyth him into wordes,
And telleth him of sondry bordes,+
And axeth him demaundes+ straunge
Wher-of she made his herte chaunge;
And to hir speche his ere he leyde
1410 And hath merveil of that she seyde.
For in proverbe and in probleme
She spak, and bad he sholde deme+
In many subtil questioun;
But he for no suggestioun
1415 Which toward him she coude stere,

1396 **In aunter if** on the chance that.
1397 **aquit** repaid.
1406 **bordes** jests.
1407 **demaundes** questions.
1412 **deme** decide.

He wolde noght oon word answere;
But as a madd man atte laste
His heed wepynge awey he caste,
And half in wraththe he bad hire go.
1420 But yet she wolde noght do so,
And in the derke forth she goth
Til she him toucheth, and he wroth,+
And after hire wyth his hond
He smot: and thus whan she him fond
1425 Disesed,+ curteisly she seyde,
"Avoy,+ my lord, I am a mayde;
And if ye wiste what I am
And out of what lignage+ I cam,
Ye wolde noght be so salvage."+
1430   Wyth that he sobreth his corage
And put awey his hevy chere.
But of hem two a man may lere
What is to be so sibb+ of blood:
Non wiste of other how it stood,
1435 And yet the fader atte laste
His herte upon this mayde caste,
That he hire loveth kyndely,
And yet he wiste nevere why.
But al was knowe er that they wente;
1440 For God, which wot her hol entente,
Her hertes bothe anon discloseth.
This kyng unto this mayde opposeth,+
And axeth first what was hir name,

1422 **wroth** became angry.
1425 **Disesed** troubled.
1426 **Avoy** fie.
1428 **lignage** lineage.
1429 **salvage** wild, fierce.
1433 **sibb** related.
1442 **opposeth** asks questions.

And wher she lerned al this game,
1445 And of what kyn that she was come.
And she, that hath his wordes nome,
Answerth and seyth, "My name is Thaise,
That was som-tyme wel at aise;+
In Tharse I was forth-drawe and fed;
1450 Ther lerned I, til I was sped
Of that I can. My fader eke
I not+ wher that I sholde him seche;
He was a kyng, men tolde me.
My moder dreynt+ was in the see."
1455 From poynt to poynt al she him tolde,
That she hath longe in herte holde
And nevere durste make hir mone,+
But only to this lord allone,
To whom hir herte can noght hele,
1460 Turne it to wo, turne it to wele,
Turne it to good, turne it to harm.
And he tho took hire in his arm:
But swich a joye as he tho made
Was nevere seen; thus be they glade
1465 That sory hadde ben to-forn.
From this day forth Fortune hath sworn
To sette him upward on the wheel:
So goth the world, now wo, now weel.+
This kyng hath founde newe grace,
1470 So that out of his derke place
He goth him up into the light,
And wyth him cam that swete wight,
His doghter Thaise, and forth anon

1448 **aise** = *ese.*
1452 **not** = *ne wot* know not.
1454 **dreynt** drowned.
1457 **make hir mone** i.e., express her grief.
1468 **weel** = *wele* happiness.

They bothe into the caban gon
1475 Which was ordeyned for the kyng;
And ther he dide of+ alle his thyng
And was arrayed royaly.
    And out he cam al openly,
Wher Athenagoras he fond,
1480 The which was lord of al the lond.
He preyeth the kyng to come and see
His castel bothe and his citee;
And thus they gon forth alle y-fere,+
This kyng, this lord, this mayden dere.
1485 This lord tho made hem riche feste
Wyth every thyng which was honeste;+
To plese wyth this worthy kyng
Ther lakketh him no manere thyng.
But yet for al his noble array,
1490 Wyfles he was into that day
As he that yet was of yong age.
So fel ther into his corage+
The lusty wo, the glade peyne
Of love, which no man restreyne
1495 Yet nevere myghte as now to-fore.
This lord thenk'th al his world forlore
But if the kyng wol don him grace;
He waiteth tyme, he waiteth place,
Him thoghte his herte wol tobreke
1500 Til he may to this mayde speke
And to hir fader eke also
For mariage: and it fel so,
That al was don right as he thoghte;
His purpose to an ende he broghte,

1476 **dide of** did off, took off.
1483 **alle y-fere** all together.
1486 **honeste** good.
1492 **corage** mind, heart.

1505 She weddeth him as for hir lord.
   Thus be they alle of oon acord.

    Whan al was done right as they wolde,
   The kyng unto his sone+ tolde
   Of Tharse thilke traiterye,+
1510 And seyde how in his companye
   His doghter and himselven eke
   Shulle go vengeaunce for-to seche.
   The shippes were redy soon,
   And whan they sawe it was to don,
1515 Wythouten lette+ of any wente+
   Wyth sayl updrawe forth they wente
   Towardes Tharse upon the tide.
   But He that wot what shal bitide,
   The heighe God, which wolde him kepe,
1520 Whan that this kyng was faste a-slepe,
   By nyghtes tyme He hath him bede+
   To seyle into an other stede:
   To Ephesim He bad him drawe,
   And as it was that tyme the lawe,
1525 He shal do ther his sacrifise;
   And eke He bad in alle wyse
   That in the temple amonges alle
   His fortune, as it is bifalle,
   Touchynge upon his doghter and his wyf
1530 He shal biknowe+ upon his lyf.
   The kyng in this avisioun
   Hath greet ymaginacioun
   What thyng it signifye may.

1508 **sone** i.e., son-in-law.
1509 **traiterye** treason.
1515 **lette** hindrance. **wente** way, device.
1521 **bede** commanded.
1530 **biknowe** make known.

And natheles, whan it was day,
1535 He bad caste anker and abod;+
And whil that he on anker rod,
The wynd, which was to-fore straunge,
Upon the poynt bigan to chaunge,
And turneth thider as it sholde.
1540 Tho knew he wel that God it wolde,
And bad the maister make him yare,+
To-fore the wynd for he wol fare
To Ephesim, and so he dede.+
And whan he cam unto the stede
1545 Wher-as he sholde londe, he londeth
Wyth al the haste he may, and fondeth+
To shapen him+ by swich a wyse,
That he may by the morwe arise
And don after the maundement+
1550 Of Him which hath him thider sent.
And in this wyse that he thoghte,
Upon the morwe so he wroghte;
His doghter and his sone he nam,
And forth unto the temple he cam
1555 Wyth a greet route+ in companye
His yiftes for-to sacrifye.
The citezeins tho herden seye
Of swich a kyng that cam to preye
Unto Diane the godesse;
1560 And lefte+ al other bisynesse
They comen thider for-to see

1535 **abod** wait, remain.
1541 **yare** ready.
1543 **dede** = *dide*.
1546 **fondeth** seeks.
1547 **To shapen him** to prepare himself.
1549 **maundement** command.
1555 **route** number, band.
1560 **lefte** i.e., having left.

The kyng and the solempnitee.
　　Wyth worthy knightes environed
The kyng himself hath abandoned+
1565　Into the temple in good entente.
The dore is up, and he in wente,
Wher-as wyth greet devocioun
Of holy contemplacioun
Wythinne his herte he made his shrift;
1570　And after that a riche yift
He offreth wyth greet reverence,
And ther in open audience
Of hem that stoden than aboute,
He tolde hem and declareth oute
1575　His hap, swich as him is bifalle—
Ther was no-thyng foryete of alle.
His wyf, as it was Goddes grace,
Which was professed+ in the place,
As she that was abbesse there,
1580　Unto his tale hath leyd hir ere.
She knew the vois and the visage:
For pure joye as in a rage+
She straughte unto him al at ones+
And fel a-swone upon the stones
1585　Wher-of the temple floor was paved.
She was anon wyth water laved,
Til she cam to hirself ageyn,
And thanne+ she bigan to seyn:
"Ha, blessed be the heighe sonde,+
1590　That I may see myn housebonde,

1564 **himself . . . abandoned** betaken himself, gone.
1578 **professed** bound by vow.
1582 **rage** violent passion.
1583 **straughte unto him al at ones** i.e., started for him suddenly.
1588 **thanne** = *than.*
1589 **sonde** decree.

That whilom he and I were oon!"
The kyng wyth that knew hire anon,
And took hire in his arm and kiste;
And al the toun thus soon it wiste.
1595 Tho was ther joye manyfold,
For every man this tale hath told
As for miracle, and were glade,
But nevere man swich joye made
As doth the kyng, which hath his wyf.
1600 And whan men herde how that hir lyf
Was saved, and by whom it was,
They wondren alle of swich a cas:
Thurgh al the lond aros the speche
Of Maister Cerymon the leche +
1605 And of the cure which he dede. +
The kyng himself tho hath him bede +
And eke this quene forth wyth him,
That he the toun of Ephesim
Wol leve and go wher as they be,
1610 For nevere man of his degree
Hath don to hem so muchel good;
And he his profit understood,
And graunteth wyth hem for-to wende.
And thus they maden ther an ende
1615 And token leve and gon to shippe
Wyth al the hole felawshipe.

    This kyng, which now hath his desire,
Seyth he wol holde his cours to Tyre.
They hadden wynd at wylle tho,
1620 Wyth topsaylcole + and forth they go,

1604 **leche** physician.
1605 **dede** = *dide*.
1606 **bede** bidden.
1620 **topsaylcole** a favorable wind.

And striken nevere til they come
To Tyre, wher-as they havene nome,+
And londen hem wyth muchel blisse.
Tho was ther many a mouth to kisse,
1625 Echoon welcometh other hom;
But whan the quene to londe com,+
And Thaise hir doghter by hir side,
The joye which was thilke tide+
Ther may no mannes tonge telle.
1630 They seyden alle, "Heer cometh the welle
Of alle wommanisshe grace."
The kyng hath take his royal place,
The quene is into chambre go;
Ther was greet feste arrayed tho.
1635 Whan tyme was, they gon to mete,
Alle olde sorwes ben foryete,
And gladden hem wyth joyes newe.
The descoloured pale hewe
Is now bicome a rody+ cheke;
1640 Ther was no myrthe for-to seche,
But every man hath that he wolde.
    The kyng, as he wel coude and sholde,
Maketh to his peple right good chere;
And after soon, as thou shalt here,
1645 A parlement he hath sumouned,
Wher he his doghter hath corouned+
Forth wyth the lord of Mitelene:
That oon is kyng, that other quene.
And thus the fadres ordinaunce
1650 This lond hath set in governaunce,

1622 **havene nome** i.e., came to harbor.
1626 **com** = *cam* came.
1628 **thilke tide** (at) that same time.
1639 **rody** ruddy, fair.
1646 **corouned** crowned.

And seyde than he wolde wende
To Tharse, for-to make an ende
Of that his doghter was bitrayed.
There-of were alle men wel payed,[+]
1655 And seyde how it was for-to don.
The shippes weren redy soon,
And strong power wyth him he took;
Up to the sky he caste his look
And saw the wynd was covenable.[+]
1660   They hale up anker wyth a cable,
The sayl on heighe, the stere[+] in honde,
And seylen til they come a-londe
At Tharse nigh to the citee;
And whan they wisten it was he,
1665 The toun hath don him reverence.
He telleth hem the violence
Which the traitour Strangulio
And Dionise him hadde do
Touchynge his doghter, as ye herde;
1670 And whan they wiste how that it ferde,
As he which pees and love soghte,
Unto the toun this he bisoghte:
To don him right in juggement.
Anon they were bothe a-sent[+]
1675 Wyth strengthe of men, and comen soon,
And as hem thoghte it was to don,
Atteynt[+] they were by the lawe
And demed for-to honge and drawe,
And brent and wyth the wynd to-blowe,
1680 That al the world it myghte knowe:

1654 **payed** pleased.
1659 **covenable** suitable.
1661 **stere** helm.
1674 **a-sent** sent for.
1677 **Atteynt** convicted.

And upon this condicioun
The doom in execucioun
Was put anon wythoute faile.
And every man hath greet merveile,
1685 Which herde tellen of this chaunce,
And thonketh Goddes purveiaunce,
Which doth mercy forth wyth justice.
Slayn is the mordrer and mordrice
Thurgh verray trouthe and rightwysnesse,
1690 And thurgh mercy sauf is simplesse⁺
Of hire whom mercy preserveth;
Thus hath he wel that wel deserveth.

Whan al this thyng is don and ended,
This kyng, which loved was and frended,
1695 A lettre hath which cam to him
By shippe from Pentapolim,
By which the lond hath to him write
That he wolde understonde and wite
How in good mynde and in good pees
1700 Deed is the kyng Artestrates,
Wher-of they alle of oon acord
Him preyden, as her lige lord,
That he the lettre wel conceive,
And come his regne to receive,
1705 Which God hath yeve him and Fortune;
And thus bisoghte the comune⁺
Forth wyth the grete lordes alle.
This kyng saw how it was bifalle,
From Tharse and in prosperitee
1710 He took his leve of that citee
And goth him into shippe ageyn:

1690 **simplesse** simplicity, humility.
1706 **comune** the common people, commonalty.

The wynd was good, the see was playn,+
Hem nedeth noght a riff+ to slake
Til they Pentapolim have take.
1715 The lond, which herde of that tidyng,
Was wonder glad of his comyng;
He resteth him a day or two,
And took his counseil to him tho,
And sette a tyme of parlement
1720 Wher al the lond of oon assent
Forth wyth his wyfe hath him corouned,
Wher alle gode him was foysouned.+
Lo, what it is to be wel grounded:
For he hath first his love founded
1725 Honestely as for-to wedde,
Honestely his love he spedde+
And hadde children wyth his wyf,
And as him liste he ledde his lyf;
And in ensaumple his lyf was write,
1730 That alle lovers myghten wite
How atte laste it shal be sene
Of love what they wolden mene.
For see now on that other side,
Antiochus wyth al his pride,
1735 Which sette his love unkyndely,+
His ende he hadde al sodeynly,
Set ayeins kynde upon vengeaunce,
And for his lust hath his penaunce.

1712 **playn** smooth.
1713 **riff** reef (of a sail).
1722 **foysouned** supplied in abundance.
1726 **spedde** advanced, fared (in).
1735 **unkyndely** unnaturally.

Floris and Blancheflour

The pagan ruler of Almeria (in Spain) takes a Christian woman captive on a raiding expedition and brings her to his court, where she soon wins favor. On the day of the Festival of Flowers (Palm Sunday), she gives birth to a daughter and the queen gives birth to a son; for this reason the son is called Floris, the daughter Blancheflour. They are brought up together, in the care of the Christian woman.

> ... Ne thurst men nevere⁺ in londe
> After fairer children fonde.⁺
> The Cristen womman fedde hem tho;
> Ful wel she lovede hem bothe two.
> 5 So longe she fedde hem y-fere⁺
> That they were of elde⁺ of sevene yere.
>
> The kyng biheeld his sone dere,
> And seyde to him on this manere,
> That harm it were muchel more
> 10 But his sone were set to lore
> On the book lettres to knowe
> As men don, bothe heighe and lowe.
> "Faire Sone," he seyde, "thou shalt lerne;
> Lo, that thou do ful yerne!"⁺
> 15 Floris answerde wyth wepyng
> As he stood bifore the kyng;
> Al wepynge seyde he,
> "Ne shal not Blancheflour lerne wyth me?

---

1 **Ne thurst men nevere** men need never.
2 **fonde** seek.
5 **y-fere** together.
6 **elde** age.
14 **yerne** eagerly, earnestly.

Ne can I noght to scole⁺ gon

20 Wythoute Blancheflour," he seyde than;
"Ne can I in no scole synge ne rede
Wythoute Blancheflour," he seyde.
The kyng seyde to his sone:
"She shal lerne, for thy love."

25 To scole they were put;
Bothe they were good of wyt.
Wonder it was of her lore,
And of her love wel the more.
The children lovede togidre so

30 They myghte nevere parte a-two.
     Whan they hadde five yere to scole go,
So wel they hadde lerned tho,
Ynough they couthe of Latyn,
And wel write on parchemyn.⁺

35 The kyng understood the grete amour
Bitwene his sone and Blancheflour,
And thoghte whan they were of age
That her love wolde not swage,⁺
Nor he myghte noght her love wythdrawe

40 Whan Floris sholde wyfe⁺ after the lawe.
The kyng to the quene seyde tho
And tolde hire of his wo—
Of his thoght and of his care
How it wolde of Floris fare.

45 "Dame," he seyde, "I telle thee my rede:⁺
I wyl that Blancheflour be don to dede.⁺
Whan that mayde is i-slawe⁺

---

19 **scole** school.
34 **parchemyn** parchment.
38 **swage** be assuaged, abated.
40 **wyfe** wive, marry.
45 **rede** plan, counsel.
46 **dede** = *deeth* death.
47 **i-slawe** = *slayn.*

And brought of hir lyf-dawe[+]
As soon as Floris may it underyete,[+]
50 Rathe[+] he wyl hire foryete:
Than may he wyfe after rede."[+]
The quene answerde than and seyde,
And thoghte wyth hir rede,
Save the mayde from the dede.[+]
55 "Sire," she seyde, "we oghte to fonde[+]
That Florens lyve wyth menske[+] in londe,
And that he lese not his honour
For the mayden Blancheflour.
Whoso myghte reve[+] that mayde clene
60 That she were broght to deeth bidene,[+]
It were muchel more honour
Thanne slee that mayde Blancheflour."
Unethes[+] the kyng graunt[+] that it be so:
"Dame, reed[+] us what is to do."
65 "Sire, we shulle our sone Floris
Sende into the lond of Mountargis;
Blithe wyl my suster be
That is lady of that contree.
And whan she wot for whom
70 That we have sent him us from,
She wyl do al hir myght,
Bothe by day and by nyght,

48 **lyf-dawe** life (-days).
49 **underyete** perceive, realize.
50 **Rathe** quickly.
51 **after rede** according to counsel.
54 **dede** = *deeth*.
55 **fonde** try (to bring about).
56 **menske** honor.
59 **reve** take away; *reve* is supplied.
60 **bidene** at once.
63 **Unethes** with difficulty. **graunt** grants.
64 **reed** advise.

To make her love so undo
As it hadde nevere ben so.
75 And, Sire," she seyde, "I rede eke
That the maydens moder make hire seke;+
That may be that other resoun,
For that ilke enchesoun,+
That she may not from hir moder go."
80 Now ben this children swithe wo,
Now they may not gon y-fere;
Dreryer+ thynges nevere non were.
Floris wepte bifore the kyng,
And seyde, "Sire, wythoute lesyng,+
85 For my harm out ye me sende,
Now she ne myghte wyth me wende.
Now we ne mote togidre go,
Al me wele+ is turned to wo!"
The kyng seyde to his sone a-plight,+
90 "Sone, wythinne this fourtenyght,
Be hir moder quik or deed,
Sikerly," he to him seyde,
"That mayde shal come thee to."
"Yee,+ Sire," he seyde, "I preye you it be so.
95 If that ye me hire sende,
I recche nevere+ whider I wende."
That the child graunted, the kyng was fayn,+

76 **make hire seke** = *sik* i.e., pretend to be sick.
78 **that ilke enchesoun** that same cause, purpose.
82 **Dreryer** more sorrowful.
84 **wythoute lesyng** truly, without falsehood.
88 **wele** joy, well-being.
89 **a-plight** at once, on his faith(?).
92 *to* is supplied.
94 **Yee** yea, yes.
96 **recche nevere** care not.
97 **fayn** glad for.

And him bitaughte⁺ his chamberleyn.
   Wyth muche honour they thider come,
As fel to⁺ a riche kynges sone.
Wel faire him received the Duk Orgas
That kyng of that castel was,
And his aunte wyth muche honour;
But evere he thoghte on Blancheflour.
Glade and blithe they ben him wyth,
But for no joye that he seeth;
Ne myghte him gladde game ne glee,
For he myghte not his lyf⁺ see.
His aunte sette him to lore
Ther as othre children wore,⁺
Bothe maydens and grome;⁺
To lerne many thider come.
Ynough he siketh, but noght he lerneth;
For Blancheflour evere he murneth.
If any man to him speke,
Love is on his herte steke.⁺
Love is at his herte rote⁺
That no-thyng is so swote:⁺
Galingale⁺ ne lycorys
Is not so swote as her love is,
Ne no-thyng ne non other flour.
So muche he thenketh on Blancheflour,
Of oon day him thynketh three,

100
105
110
115
120

98 **bitaughte** entrusted (to).
100 **As fel to** as befitted.
108 **lyf** i.e., dear one *(leef?)*.
110 **wore** = *were*.
111 **grome** men, boys.
116 **steke** fixed, fastened.
117 **rote** root.
118 **swote** sweet.
119 **Galingale** sweet cyperus.
121 *flour* is supplied.

For he ne may his love see;
125 Thus he abideth wyth muchel wo
Til the fourtenyght were go.
Whan he saw she was noght i-come,
So muchel sorwe he hath nome
That he loveth mete ne drynke,
130 Ne may non in his body synke.+
The chamberleyn sente the kyng to wite+
His sones stat, al i-write.
The kyng ful soon the wex to-brak
For-to wite+ what it spak.
135 He bigynneth to chaunge his mood,
And wel soon he understood;
And wyth wraththe he cleped the quene
And tolde hire al his tene,+
And wyth wraththe spak and seyde,
140 "Lat do brynge forth that mayde!
From the body the heed shal go!"
Than was the quene ful wo;
Than spak the quene, that gode lady,
"For Goddes love, Sire, mercy!
145 At the nexte havene+ that heer is
Ther ben chapmen+ riche, y-wis,
Marchauntz of Babyloyn+ ful riche
That wol hire beye blitheliche.+
Than mowe ye for that lovely fode+

130 **synke** i.e., be consumed.
131 **to wite** to make known.
134 **For-to wite** to know.
138 **tene** suffering, vexation.
145 **havene** harbor.
146 **chapmen** merchants.
147 **Babyloyn** i.e., Old Cairo.
148 **blitheliche** gladly.
149 **fode** creature, maiden.

150 Have muchel catel and gode;[+]
And so she may from us be broght
So that we ne slee hire noght."
Unethes the kyng graunted this,
But for sothe, so it is.

155   The kyng lett sende after the burgeys
That was hende and curteis,
And wel selle and beye couthe,
And many langages hadde in his mouthe.
Wel soon that mayde was him bitaught,[+]

160 And to the havene was she broght.
Ther have they for that mayde yolde[+]
Twenty mark of reed gold,
And a cuppe good and riche—
In al the world was non it liche:[+]

165 Ther was nevere non so wel grave—[+]
He that it made was no knave.
Ther was purtreyed on, I wene,
How Paris ledde awey the quene;
And on the covercle[+] above

170 Purtreyed was ther bothe her[+] love;
And in the pomel[+] ther-on
Stood a charboncle[+] ston.
In the world was not so depe celer[+]

---

150 **catel and gode** property and goods.
152 *ne* is supplied.
159 **bitaught** given, delivered (to).
161 **yolde** given.
164 **liche** = *like*.
165 **grave** engraved.
169 **covercle** lid.
170 **bothe her** (?) = *her bother* of them both.
171 **pomel** top.
172 **charboncle** carbuncle (precious stone).
173 **celer** cellar.

That it nolde lighte⁺ the boteler
175　To fille bothe ale and wyne;
Of silver and gold bothe good and fyne.
Eneas the kyng, that noble man,
At Troye in bataile he it wan,
And broghte it into Lumbardye
180　And yaf it his lemman, his amye.⁺
The cuppe was stole from Kyng Cesar—
A theef out of his tresour-hous it bar;
And sith that ilke same theef
For Blancheflour he it yeef;⁺
185　For he wiste to wynne swiche three,⁺
Myghte he hire brynge to his contree.
　　Now thise marchauntz seylen over the see
Wyth this mayde to her contree.
So longe they han undernome⁺
190　That to Babyloyn they ben come.
To the amyral⁺ of Babyloyn
They solde that mayde swithe soon;
Rathe and soon they were at oon:
The amyral hire boghte anon
195　And yaf for hire, as she stood uprighte,
Sevene sithes⁺ of gold hir wighte,⁺
For he thoghte wythoute wene⁺
That faire mayde have to quene;
Among his maydens in his bour
200　He hire dide wyth muche honour.

174 **lighte** light (the way for).
180 **amye** beloved.
184 **yeef** = *yaf* gave.
185 **swiche three** i.e., three such.
189 **han undernome** have persisted (in their journey).
191 **amyral** emir.
196 **sithes** times. **wighte** weight.
197 **wene** doubt.

Now thise marchauntz that may bilete⁺
And ben glade of her beyete.⁺

   Now lete we of Blancheflour be
And speke of Floris in his contree.
205 Now is the burgeys to the kyng come
Wyth the gold and his warisoun,⁺
And hath take the kyng to wold⁺
The silver and the cuppe of gold.
They lette maken in a chirche
210 A swithe faire grave werke,
And lette leye ther-upon
A newe faire paynted ston
Wyth lettres al aboute write
Wyth ful muche worshipe.
215 Whoso coude the lettres rede,
Thus they spoke and thus they seyde:
"Heer lieth swete Blancheflour
That Floris lovede par amour."
Now Floris hath undernome
220 And to his fader he is come;
In his fadres halle he is light.⁺
His fader him grette anon right,
And his moder, the quene also,
But unethe myghte he that do
225 That he ne axed wher his lemman be;⁺
Noskynnes⁺ answere chargeth⁺ he.

---

201 **that may bilete** abandoned that maiden.
202 **beyete** gain.
206 **warisoun** payment.
207 **to wold** for keeping.
221 **light** alighted.
224–225 **But unethe myghte he that do / That he ne axed wher his
lemman be** i.e., he could hardly keep from asking where his
beloved was.
226 **Noskynnes** no kind of. **chargeth** awaits.

So longe he is forth nome,
Into chambre he is come.
The maydens moder he axed right,
230 "Wher is Blancheflour, my swete wight?"
"Sire," she seyde, "for sothe, y-wis,
I ne wot wher she is."
She bithoghte hire of that lesyng+
That was ordeyned bifore the kyng.
235 "Thou gabbest+ me," he seyde tho;
"Thy gabbyng doth me muchel wo!
Tel me wher my lemman be!"
Al wepynge seyde than she,
"Sire," she seyde, "deed." "Deed!" seyde he.
240 "Sire," she seyde, "for sothe, yee."
"Allas! whan deyde that swete wight?"
"Sire, wythinne this fourtenyght
The erthe was hire leyd above,
And deed she was for thy love."
245 Floris, that was so faire and gent,
Swoned ther, verament.+
The Cristen womman bigan to crie
To Jhesu Crist and Seint Marie.
The kyng and the quene herde that cry;
250 Into the chambre they ronne on hye,+
And the quene saw hire biforn
A-swowne the child that she hadde born.
The kynges herte was al in care
That saw his sone for love so fare.
255 Whan he a-wook and speke myghte,

233 **lesyng** lying, deceit.
235 **gabbest** mock, lie (to).
243 *hire leyd above* for MS. *leide hur aboute*, modeled on Cotton Vitel
lius D. iii MS.
246 **verament** truly.
250 **on hye** in haste.
251 *saw* replaces MS. *herde*.

Sore he wepte and sore he sighte,+
And seyde to his moder, y-wis,
"Leed me ther that mayde is."
Thider they him broghte on hye;
260   For care and sorwe he wolde deye.
As soon as he to the grave cam,
Soon ther biheeld he than
And the lettres bigan to rede,
That thus speke and thus seyde:
265   "Heer lieth swete Blancheflour
That Floris lovede par amour."
Three sithes Floris swoned nouthe,+
Ne speke he myghte not wyth mouthe.
As soon as he a-wook and speke myghte,
270   Sore he wepte and sore he sighte:
"Blancheflour!" he seyde, "Blancheflour!
So swete a thyng was nevere in bour!+
Of Blancheflour is that I mene,+
For she was come of good kyn.
275   Litel and muche+ lovede thee
For thy goodnesse and thy beautee.
If deeth were delt+ aright,
We sholde be deed bothe on oon nyght;
For on oon day born we were,
280   We shulle be deed bothe y-fere.
Deeth," he seyde, "ful of envye,
And ful of al trecherie,

256 **sighte** sighed.
262 *than* (*MS.* þen) corresponds to Cot. Vit. *ther-on* (*þer-on*).
267 **nouthe** now.
272 **in bour** i.e., alive.
273 **mene** lament, mourn.
275 **Litel and muche** small and large, i.e., everyone.
277 **delt** dealt, apportioned.
279 *For* is supplied, on the model of Cot. Vit. MS.
282 *ful* is supplied, on the model of Cot. Vit. MS.

Refte thou hast me my lemman;
For sothe," he seyde, "thou are to blame.
285 She wolde have lyved, and thou noldest,+
And fayn wolde I deye, and+ thou woldest.
After deeth clepe namore I nyl,+
But slee myself now I wyl."
    His knyf he breyde+ out of his sheeth;
290 Himself he wolde have don to deeth,
And to herte he hadde it smyten
Ne hadde his moder it underyeten.+
Than the quene fel him upon
And the knyf she from him nam.
295 She refte him of his litel knyf
And saved ther the childes lyf.
Forth the quene ran, al wepynge,
Til she cam to the kyng;
Than seyde the gode lady,
300 "For Goddes love, sire, mercy!
Of twelve children have we non
On lyve now but this oon;
And bettre it were she were his make+
Thanne he were deed for hir sake."
305 "Dame, thou seyst sooth," seyde he;
"Sith it may non other be,
Lever me were she were his wyf
Thanne I lost my sones lyf."
Of this word the quene was fayn,
310 And to hir sone she ran ageyn.

---

285 **noldest** = *ne woldest* willed (it) not.
286 **and** if. After this line the Cot. Vit. MS. adds twelve more lines of
    Floris' complaint.
287 **nyl** = *ne wyl* will not.
289 **breyde** drew quickly.
292 **underyeten** perceived.
294 *she* is supplied, on the model of Cot. Vit. MS.
303 **make** mate.

"Floris, Sone, glad mak thee:
Thy leef⁺ thou shalt on-lyve see.
Floris, Sone, thurgh engyn⁺
Of thy fadres rede and myn,
315 This grave lette we make,⁺
Leve Sone, for thy sake:
If thou that mayde foryete woldest,
After oure rede wyfe thou sholdest."
Now every word she hath him tolde
320 How that they that mayden solde.
"Is this sooth, my Moder dere?"
"For sothe," she seyde, "she is not heer."
That rowe⁺ ston adoun they leyde
And sawe that ther was not the mayde.
325 "Now, Moder, I thenke that I lyve may,
Ne shal I reste nyght ne day—
Nyght ne day, ne no stounde—⁺
Til I have my lemman founde.
Hire to sechen I wol wende
330 Thogh it were to the worldes ende!"

To the kyng he goth to take his leve,
And his fader bad him bileve.⁺
"Sire, I wyl lette⁺ for no wynne;
Me to bidden it it were greet synne."
335 Than seyde the kyng, "Sith it is so,
Sith thou wylt non other do,
Al that thee nedeth we shulle thee fynde.⁺

312 **leef** beloved.
313 **engyn** contrivance.
315 **lette we make,** we caused to be made.
323 **rowe** rough.
324 *ther* is supplied, on the model of Cot. Vit. MS.
327 **stounde** space of time.
332 **bileve** remain.
333 **lette** keep from (it).
337 **fynde** provide.

Jhesu thee of care unbynde."
"Leve Fader," he seyde, "I telle thee
340 Al that thou shalt fynde me.
Thou most me fynde, at my devise,+
Sevene horses alle of pris;
And two i-charged upon the mold+
Bothe wyth silver and wyth gold,
345 And two i-charged wyth moneye
For-to spenden by the weye,
And three wyth clothes riche
The beste of al the kyngesriche.+
Sevene horses and sevene men,
350 And three knaves wythoute hem;+
And thyn owene chamberleyn
That is a wel noble swayn: +
He can us wisse and us rede.+
As marchauntz we shulle us lede."
355 His fader was an hende kyng;
The cuppe of gold he dide him bryng,
That ilke selve cuppe of gold
That was Blancheflour for yolde.+
"Have this, Sone," seyde the kyng;
360 "Heer-wyth thou mayst that swete thyng
Wynne, so may bitide—
Blancheflour wyth the white side,
Blancheflour that faire may."
The kyng lett sadel a palfrey,
365 The oon half+ so white as milk,

338 This is an anomaly, since it is spoken by the pagan king.
341 **devise** disposal.
343 **upon the mold** on the earth (a rhyme tag).
348 **kyngesriche** kingdom, realm.
350 **wythoute hem** i.e., in addition.
352 **swayn** (young) servant.
353 **us wisse and us rede** direct and advise us.
358 **yolde** given (in payment).
365 **half** side.

And that other reed as silk.
I ne can telle noght
How richely that sadel was wroght.
The arsoun+ was of gold fyne;
370 Stones of vertue stode ther-inne,
Bigonne aboute wyth orphrays.+
The quene was kynde and curteis:
Caste hire toward the kyng,
And of hir fynger she breyde+ a ryng:
375 "Have now this ilke ryng.
Whil it is thyne, dout+ no-thyng
Of fyr brennyng ne water in the see,
Ne iren ne steel shal dere+ thee."
He took his leve for-to go.
380 Ther was ful muchel wo;
They made hem non other chere
Thanne her sone were leyd in bere.
    Forth he went wyth al his mayn;+
Wyth him went the chamberleyn.
385 Forth to the havene+ they ben i-come,
And ther haven her inn i-nome
Ther Blancheflour was that other nyght.
Wel richely they ben i-dight.
The lord of the inn was wel hende;
390 The child+ he sette next the ende

369 **arsoun** saddle-bow.
371 **orphrays** orphrey.
374 **breyde** drew.
376 **dout** fear, doubt.
378 **dere** injure, harm.
383 **mayn** might.
385 **havene** harbor.
385–6 These lines are from the Cambridge MS. Gg. 4.27.2, replacing *So haue þey her hauyn nome / þat þey ben to þe hauyn come.*
387 *that other,* from Camb. MS., replacing *al.*
390 **child** youth.

In al the faireste sete.
Alle they dronken and alle they ete.
Ete and drynke mighte he noght—
On Blancheflour was al his thoght.

395 The lady of that inn underyat+
That the child murnynge sat,
And seyde to hir lord wyth stille dreme,+
"Sire, nym thou now good yeme+
How the child murnynge sitteth:

400 Mete and drynke he foryeteth,
Litel he eteth and lasse he drynketh.
He is no marchaunt, as me thinketh."
To Floris than seyde she,
"Al ful of murnyng I thee see.

405 Ther sat ther this endre day+
Blancheflour, that swete may.
Hider was that mayde broght
Wyth marchauntz that hire hadde boght;
Hider they broghte that mayde swete:

410 They wolde have sold hire for beyete.+
Thou art hire like of alle thyng,
Bothe of semblaunt+ and of murnyng."
Whan Floris herde speke of his lemman,
Was he nevere so glad a man,

415 And in his herte bigan to lighte;
The cuppe he lett fille anon-righte;
"Dame," he seyde, "the vessel is thyne,
Bothe the cuppe and the wyne:

---

395 **underyat** perceived. *inn* supplied, Auckinleck MS. has *hous*.
397 **stille dreme** quiet sound, voice.
398 **nym . . . yeme** take care, heed. *thou* is supplied.
402 *no,* from Camb. MS., replacing *a*.
405 **endre day** day just past, recently.
410 **beyete** gain.
411 Line from Camb. MS. replacing *To Babyloyne þey wylle hur bryng*.
412 **semblaunt** appearance, looks.

The wyne and the gold eke,
420 For thou of my lemman speke.
On hire I thoghte, for hire I sighte; +
I ne wiste wher I hire fynde myghte.
Wynd ne weder shal me assoyne +
That I ne shal seche hire in Babyloyne."
425   Now Floris resteth him al a nyght.
At morne, whan it was day light,
He dide him into the wilde flode. +
Wynd and weder wyth him stode;
Soon so Floris cam to londe,
430 Ther he thonked Goddes sonde +
To the londe ther his lemman is:
Him thoghte he was in paradys.
Soon to Floris tidyng men tolde
That the amyral + wolde feste holde;
435 His erles, barouns, comen sholde,
And alle that wolde of him londe holde,
For-to herken his heste, +
And for-to honoure his feste.
Glad was Floris of that tidyng:
440 He hoped to cam to that gestnyng, +
If he myghte in that halle
His lemman see among hem alle.
   Now to that citee Floris is come;
Faire he hath his inn i-nome
445 At a paleys—was it non liche. +

421 **sighte** sighed.
423 **assoyne** prevent, excuse.
427 **flode** waters.
430 **sonde** sending (him).
431 *lemman,* in both Auch. and Camb. MSS., replacing *lyf ynne.*
434 **amyral** emir.
437 **heste** command.
440 **gestnyng** entertainment.
445 **liche** = *like.*

The lord of that inn was ful riche;
He hadde ben fer and wide.
The child he sette next his side
In al the fairest sete.
450 Alle they dronken and ete,
Alle that ther-inne were;
Alle they made good chere.
They ete and dronken echoon wyth other,
But Floris thoghte al on an other;
455 Ete ne drynke he myghte noght—
On Blancheflour was al his thoght.
Than spak the burgeys
That was hende and curteis:
"O Child, me thinketh wel
460 That muche thou thenkest on my catel."+
"Nay, Sire, on catel thenke I noght"
(On Blancheflour was al his thoght),
"But I thenke on al wyse
For-to fynde my marchaundise.
465 And yet it is the moste wo,
Whan I it fynde, I shal it forgo."
Than spak the lord of that inn,
"This endre day ther sat heer-inne
That faire mayde Blancheflour,
470 Bothe in halle and in bour.
Evere she made murnynge chere
And bement+ Floris, hir lyf fere;+
Joye ne blisse made she non,
But for Floris she made hir mon."+

454 *on* is supplied.
460 **catel** property.
463–466 Floris' answer is in the form of a riddle; he gives the same
      answer to subsequent questioning.
472 **bement** bemoaned. **fere** companion.
474 **mon** = *mone* complaint.

475 Floris took a coppe of silver clere[+]
A mantel of scarlet wyth menyvere:[+]
"Have this, Sire, to thyn honour:
Thou may thonke it[+] Blancheflour.
He myghte make myn herte glad
480 That coude me telle whider she is lad."[+]
"Child, to Babyloyn she is broght;
The amyral hire hath boght.
He yaf for hire, as she stood uprighte,
Sevene sithes of gold hir wighte;
485 For he thenketh, wythoute wene,[+]
That faire mayde have to quene.
Among his maydens in his tour
He hire dide, wyth muche honour."

Now Floris resteth him ther al nyght,
490 Til on the morwe the day was light.
He ros on the morwenyng;
He yaf his hoste an hundred shillyng,
To his hoste and to his hostesse,
And took his leve, and faire dide kisse;
495 And yerne his hoste he bisoghte
That he him helpe, if he myghte oght—
If he myghte, wyth any gynne,[+]
That faire mayde to him wynne.
"Child," he seyde, "to a brigge[+] thou shalt come;
500 The senpere[+] fynde at home:
He woneth at the brigges ende.

475 **clere** bright.
476 **menyvere** miniver.
478 **thonke it** i.e., thank for it.
480 **lad** led (to).
485 **wene** doubt.
497 **gynne** contrivance.
499 **brigge** bridge.
500 **senpere** man of good rank (the bridge keeper).

Curteis man he is, and hende;
We ben brethren, and trouthes plight:
He can thee wisse and rede aright.
505 Thou shalt bere him a ryng
From myself, to tokenyng,
That he helpe thee in bour and halle
As it were my self bifalle."
Floris taketh the ryng and nymeth leve,
510 For longe he wolde noght bileve.+
By that it was undren heighe,+
The brigge cam he swithe nigh.
The senperes name was Darys.
Floris greete him wel faire, y-wis,
515 And he him the ryng raughte,+
And ful faire it him bitaughte.+
Thurgh the token of that ilke ryng
Floris hadde ful faire gestnyng,+
Of fissh and flessh and tendre breed,+
520 Of wyne, bothe white and reed.
And evere Floris sat ful colde,
And Darys bigan the child biholde:
"Leve Child, what may this be,
Thus thoghtful, as I thee see?
525 Art thou noght al in fere,+
That thou makest thus sory chere,
Or thou likest noght this inn?"
Than Floris answerde him:

510 **bileve** remain.
511 **undren heighe** high noon.
515 **raughte** handed over.
516 **bitaughte** gave.
518 **gestnyng** entertainment.
519 **breed** bread.
525 **in fere** (?) well. *Art* replaces *And;* the corresponding line in the Camb. MS. reads (normalized): *Thou nart [= ne art] noght glad of thy soupere.*

117

"Yis, Sire, by Goddes ore,+
530 So good ne hadde I many day yore;+
God lete me abide that day
That I thee quite+ wel may!
But I thenke on alle wyse
Moste upon my marchaundise;
535 And yet it is most wo,
Whan I it fynde, I shal it forgo."
"Child, woldest thou telle me thy greef?
To hele thee me were ful leef."+
Every word he hath him told,
540 How the mayde was from him sold,
And how he was of Spayn a kynges sone,
For greet love thider i-come
To fonde, wyth queyntise and wyth gynne,+
Blancheflour for-to wynne.
545   "Now," seyth Darys, "thou art a folt"+—
And for a fool the child he halt.+
"Now I wot how it goth:
Thou desirest thyn owene deeth.
The amyral hath to his justynges+
550 Other half hundred+ of riche kynges,
And the alder-richest+ kyng
Durste not bigynne swich a thyng.
If amyral myghte it understonde,
He sholde be drawe in his owene londe.

529 ore mercy, grace.
530 many day yore a long while.
532 quite repay.
538 me . . . ful leef very pleasing to me.
543 queyntise and . . . gynne artfulness and trickery.
545 folt dunce.
546 halt holds, considers.
549 justynges jousts, tournaments.
550 Other half hundred half a hundred other.
551 alder-richest richest-of-all.

555   Aboute Babyloyn, I wene,
      Sixe longe myle and ten; +
      At every myle is a wal ther-at,
      Sevene sithes twenty yate; +
      And twenty toures ther ben inne,
560   That every day chepyng+ is inne;
      Every day and nyght thurghout the yere
      The chepyng is iliche plenere. +
      And thogh alle the men that ben born
      Hadde on her lyf sworn
565   To wynne that mayde faire and free,
      Alle shulle they deye, so moot I thee. +
      In that bour, in myd-ward righte,
      Stondeth a tour, I thee plighte: +
      An hundred fadme+ it is heighe;
570   Whoso biholdeth it, fer or nigh,
      An hundred fadme it is y-fere;
      It is mad wythoute pere+
      Of lym and of marble-ston;
      In al this world is swich non.
575   Now is the morter mad so wel,
      Ne may it breke iren ne steel.
      The pomel+ that above is leyd,
      It is mad wyth muchel pride,

---

556 **Sixe . . . myle and ten** (the distance is) six and ten miles.
558 **yate** gates.
560 **chepyng** trading, marketing.
562 **iliche plenere** always in full (progress).
566 **so moot I thee** as I hope to prosper.
567 MS. reads *pyꝣt* placed.
568 **plighte** pledge, assure.
569 **fadme** fathoms.
572 **pere** peer, equal.
575 ff. The Camb. MS. has additional lines of description here, including mention of a well and a pipe to carry water (see line 875 of this edition).
577 **pomel** knob, finial.

That man ne thar in the toure berne+
580 Nother torche ne lanterne,
Swich a pomel was ther bigonne:+
It shyneth a-nyght as doth the sonne.
   Now ben in that ilke tour
Two and fourty noble bour;+
585 Wel were that ilke man
That myghte wone+ in that oon!
Ne durste him nevere more, y-wis,
Covete after more blisse.
Now ben ther sergeaunts+ in that stage+
590 That serven the maydens of heighe parage:+
But no sergeaunt may serve ther-inne
That bereth in his breech+ that gynne
To serve hem day and nyght,
But he be as a capon dight.
595 At the yate is a yate-ward;+
He is no fool ne no coward:
He is wonder proude wyth-alle;
Every day he goth in riche palle.+
   And the amyral hath a wonder wone+
600 . . . .
   Every yeer to have a newe wyf;

579 **ne thar . . . berne** need not burn.
581 **bigonne** done, set.
584 **bout** bowers, chambers.
586 **wone** dwell.
589 **sergeaunts** servants. **stage** place.
590 **parage** lineage.
592 **breech** breeches.
595 **yate-ward** gate-ward, -keeper.
596 Line patterned after Auch. MS. to expand *He is not a cowarde.*
598 **riche palle** fine cloth.
599 **wone** custom.
600 A gratuitous line occurs here, *þat he þat is come of Cristendome,* the meaning of which is dubious.

Than he loveth his quene as his lyf.
Than shulle men brynge doun of the tour
Alle the maydens of greet honour,
605 And brynge hem into an orcherd,
The faireste of al myddel-erd:+
Ther-inne is many foweles song;
Man myghte lyve ther-inne longe.
Aboute the orcherd is a wal,
610 The fouleste ston is cristal;
And a welle spryngeth ther-inne
That is made wyth muchel gynne.
The welle is of muchel pris:
The stremes come from Paradys;
615 The gravel of the ground is precious stones,
And alle of vertue for the nones.
Now is the welle of muchel ey:+
If a womman come that is forlay+
And she be don to the streme
620 For-to wasshe hir hondes clene,
The water wyl yelle+ as it were wood+
And bicome reed as blood.
On what mayde the water fareth so,
Soon she shal to deeth be do.
625 Tho that ben maydens clene+
They may wasshe ther-inne, I wene;
The water wol stonde faire and clere:
To hem maketh it no daunger.+
At the welles heed stondeth a tree,
630 The faireste that on erthe may be;

606 **myddel-erd** the earth.
617 **ey** awe, fear.
618 **forlay** adulterous.
621 **yelle** = (?) *welle* surge. **wood** mad.
625 **clene** i.e., pure.
628 **daunger** resistance.

It is cleped the Tree of Love;
Floures and blosmes spryngen above.
Than they that maydens clene be,
They shulle be broght under the tree,
635 And which-so+ falleth the firste flour
Shal be quene wyth muche honour.
And if ther any mayden is
That the amyral telleth+ of more pris,
The flour shal be to hire sent
640 Thurgh the art of enchauntement.
The amyral cheseth hem by the flour,
And evere he herkneth after Blancheflour."
    Three sithes Floris swoned anon
Right bifore hem everichoon.
645 Whan he a-wook and speke myghte,
Sore he wepte and sore he sighte,
And seyde, "Darys, I worth+ now deed
But that I hope of thee som reed."+
"Leve Sone, wel I see
650 That thy truste is muche on me.
Than is the beste rede that I can—
Other rede ne can I non—
Wend to-morne to the tour
As thou were a good gynour;+
655 Tak on thyn honde square and scantilon+
As thou were a freemason.
Bihold the tour up and doun;

---

635 **which-so** i.e., on that one which. *firste* supplied from Camb. MS.
637 Line emended on the model of Auch. and Camb. MSS., from ȝif *any*
    mayden þer is.
638 **telleth** accounts.
647 **worth** shall become.
648 **reed** = *rede* help.
649 *wel I see* for MS. *wyl ȝe see.*
654 **gynour** one who contrives machines.
655 **scantilon** measure, pattern.

The porter is cruel and feloun;[+]
Wel soon he wyl come to thee
660 And axe what manere man thou be,
And bere[+] on thee felonye
And seye thou art come to be a spye.
And thou shalt answere swetely
And seye to him wel myldely;
665 Sey thou art a gynour
To biholde that faire tour,
For-to loke and for-to fonde
To make swich an other in thy londe.
Wel soon he wyl come thee nere
670 And wyl bidde thee pleye at the chekkere.[+]
Whan thou art at chekkere broght,
Wythoute silver be thou noght;
Thou shalt have redy wyth thee
Twenty mark biside thy knee.
675 If thou wynne oght of his,
Thou tel ther-of litel pris;[+]
And if he wynne oght of thyn,
Loke thou leve it wyth him.
So thou shalt, al wyth gynne,[+]
680 The porters love for sothe wynne,
That he thee helpe on this day:
But[+] he thee helpe, no man may.
Wel yerne he wyl thee bidde and preye
Come an other day to pleye;
685 Thou shalt seye thou wylt so;

658 **feloun** fierce, deadly.
661 **bere** charge, impute.
664 *wel* supplied on the model of the Auch. and Camb. MSS.
670 **chekkere** chess.
676 **Thou tel ther-of-litel pris** i.e., discount it.
679 **wyth gynne** with a trick.
682 **But** unless

Thou shalt take wyth thee swiche two.[+]
The thridde day, tak an hundred pound
And thy cuppe hol and sound;
Yif him markes and poundes of thy male[+]—
690   Of thy tresour tel thou no tale;[+]
Wel yerne he wyl thee bidde and preye
To laye[+] thy cuppe, and to pleye.
Thou shalt answere alderfirst,[+]
Lenger to pleye thee ne list.
695   Ful muche he wyl for the cuppe bede,[+]
If he myghte the bettre spede;
Thou shalt it blithely yeve him
If[+] it be of gold fyne;
And he wol ful muche love thee,
700   And to thee bowe also, pardee,
That he wyl falle to thy foot,
And bicome thyne, if he moot,
And homage thou shalt fonge[+]
And the trouthe of his honde."

705   As he seyde, he dide y-wis;
And as he ordeyned, so it is:
The porter is Floris man bicome
For his gold and his warisoun.[+]
Floris seyde, "Now art thou my mon,[+]
710   Al my truste is thee upon;

686 **swiche two** twice as much (money).
689 **male** wallet.
690 **tel thou no tale** i.e., take no account.
692 **laye** wager.
693 **alderfirst** first of all.
695 **bede** bid, offer.
698 **If** though.
703 **fonge** receive.
708 **warisoun** reward.
709 **mon** companion.

Now my counseil I wyl thee shewe;
Reed+ me right, if thou be trewe."
Now every word he hath him told—
How the mayde was from him sold,

715 And how he was of Spayn a kynges sone,
For greet love thider i-come
To fonden, wyth som gynne,
That faire mayde for-to wynne.
The porter hath herd, and sore sighte,+

720 And seyde, "I am bitrayed arighte;
Thurgh thy catel I am desmayed;
Ther-fore I am wel yvele apayed.+
Now I wot how it goth:
For thee shal I suffre deeth!

725 I shal thee fayle never-mo,
The while+ I may ride and go.
Thy forewardes+ shal I holde alle,
What so evere may bifalle.
Wend now hom to thyn inn,

730 Whil I bithenke me of som gynne;
Bitwene this and the thridde day
Fonde I shal what I do may."
Floris spak and wepte among
And thoghte the terme al to long.

735   The porter thoghte the beste reed,+
And lett gadre floures in a meed—
He wiste it was the maydens wylle.
Two lepes+ he lett of floures fille;
That was the beste rede, as him thoghte tho,

---

712 **Reed** advise.
719 **sighte** sighed.
722 **wel yvele apayed** very ill pleased.
726 **The while** i.e., any time.
727 **forewardes** agreements.
735 **reed** = *rede* plan.
738 **lepes** baskets.

740 Floris in that oon leep+ to do.
Two maydens the leep bere;
So hevy charged nevere they were,
And bade God yeve him yvel fyn—+
To many floures he dide ther-inne!
745 To Blancheffoures chambre they sholde tee;+
They yede to an other, and lette that be.
They sholde have gon to Blancheflour,
And yede to swete Clarys bour,
And cursede him so fele+ broghte to honde;
750 They yede hom and lette hem stonde.
Clarys to the leep come wolde
The floures to hondle and to biholde.
Floris wende+ it hadde ben his swete wight:
Of the leep he stirte upright,
755 And the mayde, al for drede,
Bigan to shrille and to grede.+
Whan he saw it was not she,
Into the leep ageyn stirte he,
And heeld him bitrayed clene:
760 Of his lyf tolde+ he not a bene.
Ther come maydens and to Clarys lepe+
By ten, by twelve, on an hepe,+
And they axede what hire were,+
And why she made swich a bere.+
765 Clarys bithoghte hire anon-right

740 **leep** basket.
743 **fyn** ending.
745 **tee** go.
749 **him so fele** i.e., him who so many flowers.
753 **wende** supposed.
756 **shrille and . . . grede** shriek and cry.
760 **tolde** counted.
761 **lepe** ran.
762 **on an hepe** in crowds.
763 **what hire were** i.e., what was her trouble.
764 **bere** outcry.

That it was Blancheflour the white,
And yaf the maydens answere anon,
That to hir chambre were gon,
That to the leep come she wolde
770 The floures to hondle and to biholde;
"And er I it ever wiste,
A boterflye cam ayeins my brest!
I was so sore adrede[+] than
That I loude crie gan."
775 The maydens ther-of hadden glee
And turnde hem and lette hire be.
And soon as the maydens were gon,
To Blancheflour she yede anon,
And seyde boldely to Blancheflour:
780 "Felawe, com and see a faire flour!
Swich a flour thee shal wel like—
Hast thou it seen a lite."
"Awey, Clarys!" quod Blancheflour,
"To scorne me it is non honour.
785 I here, Clarys, wythoute gabbe[+]
That the amyral wyl me to wyf habbe;[+]
But that day shal nevere be
That he shal evere have me—
That I shal be of love so untrewe,
790 Ne chaunge my love for no newe;
For no love, ne for non ey,[+]

766 Auch. MS. reads . . . *Blaunchefiour swete wist,* an improvement in sense and rhyme.

772 The MS. reads *An Otter fleyʒ a-geynst my brest;* Camb. MS. reads *þer fliste vt a buterfliʒe;* Auch. MS. reads *A boterfleʒe toʒain me fluste.*

773 **adrede** afraid.

774 *gan* for MS. *can.*

785 **gabbe** lie, boasting.

786 **habbe** = *have.*

791 **ey** fear.

Forsake Floris in his contree.
Now[+] I shal swete Floris mysse,
Ne shal non other of me have blisse."
795 Clarys stood and biheeld that routhe[+]
And the trewenesse of hir trouthe,
And seyde, "Lady Blancheflour,
Go we see that ilke flour."
To the leep[+] they wente bo;[+]
800 Joyeful man was Floris tho,
For he hadde herd al this.
Of that leep he stirte, y-wis;
Wel soon Blancheflour chaunged hewe:
Either of hem other knew.
805 Wythoute speche togidre they lepe,[+]
And clypte and kiste wonder swete.
Clarys biheeld al this,
Her countenaunce and her blisse,
And seyde than to Blancheflour:
810 "Felawe, knowest thou oght this flour?
She shal conne[+] ful muche of art
That thou woldest ther-of yeve part."
Now Blancheflour and Floris,
Bothe thise swete thynges, y-wis,
815 Crien hir mercy, al wepynge,
That she ne wreye[+] hem to the kyng.
"Ne doute no more of me in alle
Thanne it were myself bifalle.
Witeth ye wel witterly[+]

792 *In his contree* is a rhyme tag and should not be understood literally.
793 **Now** i.e., now that.
795 **routhe** i.e., pitiful sight.
799 **leep** basket. **bo** both.
805 **lepe** leaped, ran.
811 **conne** know.
816 **wreye** betray.
819 **witterly** plainly.

820   Hele+ I wyl youre druery."+
      To a bedde they ben broght
      That is of palle and of silk i-wroght,
      And ther they sette hem doun
      And drowe hemselve al a-roum:+
825   Ther was no man that myghte rade+
      The joye that they two made.
      Floris than to speke bigan,
      And seyde, "Lord, that madest man,
      I it thonke Goddes Sone
830   That al my care I have overcome.
      Now me leef I have i-founde,
      Of al my care I am unbounde."
      Clarys hem served al at wylle,
      Bothe dernely+ and stille.

835   Clarys wyth the white side
      Ros up on the morne tide,
      And cleped after Blancheflour
      To wende wyth hire into the tour.
      She seyde, "I am comynge,"
840   But hir answere was slepynge.+
      The amyral hadde swich a wone+
      That every day sholde come
      Two maydens of her bour
      Up to him into the tour
845   Wyth water and cloth and basin
      For-to wasshe his hondes inne.
      That day they servede him faire;

820 **Hele** conceal. **druery** love.
824 **a-roum** aside.
825 **rade** = *rede* reckon, describe.
834 **dernely** secretly.
840 **slepynge** in sleep.
841 **wone** custom.

An other day cam an other paire;
But moste were woned⁺ into the tour
850 Clarys and Blancheflour.
Clarys cam than allone:
The amyral axed anon,
"Wher is Blancheflour so free?
Why cometh she not hider wyth thee?"
855 "Sire," she seyde anon-right,
"She hath waked⁺ al this nyght,
And i-cried and i-loke,⁺
And i-rad⁺ on hir boke,
And i-bede⁺ to God hir orisoun
860 That He yeve thee His benisoun
And that He holde long thy lyf.
And now the mayde slepeth swithe;
She slepeth so faste, that mayden swete,
That she may not comen yet."
865 "Certes," seyde the kyng,
"Now is she a swete thyng.
Wel oghte me yerne⁺ hire to wyf
That so preyeth for my lyf."
    An other day Clarys erly arist;⁺
870 That Blancheflour wel wiste,
And seyde, " I come anon,"
Whan Clarys hire clepe bigan—
And fel in a slepe newe.
Soon after it made hem to rewe!

849 **woned** accustomed (to go).
856 **waked** i.e., been awake.
857 **i-loke** gazed.
858 **i-rad** read.
859 **i-bede** prayed.
867 **yerne** desire.
869 **arist** = *ariseth.*

875   Clarys to the piler[+] cam;
      A basin of gold in hond she nam,
      And cleped after Blancheflour
      To wende wyth hire into the tour.
      The amyral axed after Blancheflour:
880   "What! is she not comen yet?
      Now she me douteth[+] al to lite."
      Forth he cleped his chamberleyn
      And bad him wende wyth his mayn
      To wite why she wyl not come
885   As she was woned bifore to don.
      The chamberleyn is forth i-nome;[+]
      Into the chambre he is come
      And stondeth bifore hir bedde,
      And fyndeth ther, nebbe to nebbe,[+]
890   Wel faste i-clipt,[+] and mouth to mouthe.
      To the amyral it was soon couthe;
      Up into the toure he staw[+]
      And tolde his lord al that he saw.
      The amyral lett him his swerd brynge,
895   For wite he wolde of that tidyng.
      He went to hem ther they laye:
      Yet was she a-slepe ther ay.[+]
      The amyral lett the clothes doun caste

875 **piler** i.e., a pipe to supply water. (The pipe mentioned earlier in the Camb. MS., in a passage that would follow line 576 in the present numbering.)
881 **douteth** fears.
885 *bifore* supplied from Auch. MS.
886 **forth i-nome** i.e., went forth.
889 **nebbe to nebbe** face to face. Perhaps *ther* should read *hem*.
890 **i-clipt** embraced. Egerton and Auch. MSS. repeat *nebbe to nebbe;* the present reading is from the Camb. MS.
892 **staw** ascended.
897 **ay** still, yet.

A litel benethe her brest,
900 And soon he knew anon
That oon was womman, that other grome.+
He quaked for tene+ ther he stood:
Hem to sleen was his mood.
Yet he thoghte, er he hem quelle,+
905 What they were, they sholde him telle,
And sith he wyl wyth doom hem don.+
The children wakede swithe soon,
And sawe the swerd over hem drawe;
They ben adrede and in awe.
910 Than seyde Floris to Blancheflour,
"Of oure lyf is no socour."+
But they criede him mercy swithe
For-to lengthe her lyve.
Up he bad hem sitte bothe
915 And do on bothe her clothe.
Sith he dide hem bynde faste
And in prisoun lett hem be caste.

Now hath he after his barouns sent
To wreke him after juggement.+
920 Now have the barouns undernome,+
And to the amyral they ben come.
He stood up among hem alle
Wyth semblaunt wroth wythal,
And seyde, "Lordynges, wyth muche honour

901 **grome** (young) man.
902 **tene** anger.
904 **quelle** kill. *quelle* (present subjunctive) for MS. quelde (killed), indicated by rhyme and paralleled in Auch. MS.
906 **wyth doom hem don** i.e., judge them.
911 **socour** help.
919 **after juggement** according to law.
920 **undernome** set out.

925 Ye herde speke of Blancheflour:
That I boghte hire dere a-plighte +
For sevene sithes of gold hir wighte;
For I wende, wythoute wene, +
That faire mayde to have had to quene.

930 Among my maydens in my tour
I hire dide wyth muche honour.
Bifore hir bed myself I cam:
I fond ther-inne a naked man.
Than were they to me so lothe +

935 I thoghte to have slayn hem bothe,
I was so wroth and so wood;
Yet I wythdrough myn hote blood
Til I have sent after you, by assent
To wreke me wyth juggement.

940 Now yet ye wite how it is gon,
Wreke me soon of my fon." +
Than spak a kyng of that londe,
"We have herd al this shame and shonde; +
But er we hem to dethe deme,

945 Lat us hem see, if it thee queme, +
What they wolde speke or segge, +
If they wol oght ageyn us legge: +
It were noght right juggement
Wythoute answere make acoupement. +

950 Til this is herd of more and lasse,

926 **a-plighte** indeed.
928 **wythoute wene** without doubt.
934 **lothe** hateful.
941 **fon** foes.
943 **shonde** shame, harm.
945 **queme** please.
946 **segge**= *seye*.
947 **legge** plead, allege.
949 **acoupement** accusation.

What mystere is⁺ to bere witnesse?"
After the children have they sent—
To brenne hem was his entent;
Two sergeaunts hem gonne brynge
955   Toward her dethes al wepynge.
Drery⁺ bothe thise children go;
Either bemeneth⁺ othres wo.
Than seyde Floris to Blancheflour,
"Of oure lyf is no socour:
960   If kynde⁺ of man it thole myghte,⁺
Twyes I sholde deye wyth righte,
Ones for myself, an other for thee,
For thy deeth thou hast for me."
Blancheflour seyde tho,
965   "The gilt is myn of oure wo."
     Floris drough forth that ryng
That his moder him yaf at her partyng:
"Have this ryng, lemman myne,
Thou shalt not deye whil it is thyne."
970   Blancheflour seyde tho,
"So ne shal it nevere go
That this ryng shal helpe me
And the deeth I on thee see."
Floris that ryng hire raughte,⁺
975   And she it him ageyn bitaughte.⁺
Nother ne wyl other deed seen:
They lette it falle hem bitwene.
A kyng cam after; a ryng he fond,
And broghte it forth in his hond.

---

951 **What mystere is** i.e., what need is there.
955 *dethes* is supplied.
956 **Drery** sorrowful.
957 **bemeneth** bemoans.
960 **kynde** (the) nature. **it thole myghte** might endure it.
974 **raughte** handed (to).
975 **bitaughte** gave.

980 Thus the children wepynge come
To the fyr and her doom.
   Bifore the folk they were broght;
Drery was her bother+ thoght.
Ther was non so sterne man
985 That the children loked on,
That they ne wolde, al wel fawe,+
Her juggement have wythdrawe,
And wyth greet catel hem beye,+
If they durste speke or seye:
990 For Floris was so faire a yongelyng,
And Blancheflour so swete a thyng,
Ther wiste no man wher+ hem were wo
For no semblaunt that they made tho.
   The amyral was so wroth and wood,
995 Ne myghte he noght kele+ his hote blood.
He bad the children faste be bounde
And into the fyr slonge.+
That ilke kyng that the ryng fond,
To the amyral he spak and rounde,+
1000 And wolde hem save to the lyve,
And tolde how for the ryng they gonne stryve.
The amyral lett hem ageyn clepe,+
For he wolde here hem speke,
And axed Floris what he hette;+
1005 And he tolde him ful skete;+

983 **her bother** of both of them.
986 **fawe** willingly.
988 **beye** redeem.
992 **wher** whether.
994 *wroth and* supplied on the model of Auch. and Camb. MSS.
995 **kele** cool.
997 **slonge** flung.
999 **rounde** whispered.
1002 **lett hem ageyn clepe** had them called back.
1004 **hette** was called.
1005 **skete** quickly.

"Sire," he seyde, "if it were thy wylle,
Thou ne getest not that mayde to spille.+
But, gode Sire, quel thou me,
And lat that mayde on-lvye be."
1010 Blancheflour seyde binne,+
"The gilt of oure dedes is myn."
The amyral seyde tho,
"Y-wis, ye shulle deye bo!"+
His swerd he breyde out of his sheeth
1015 The children to have don to deeth.
Blancheflour putte forth hir swire,+
And Floris dide hire ageyn to tire,+
And seyde, "I am a man, I shal bifore.
Wyth wrong+ hast thou thy lyf i-lore!"+
1020 Floris forth his swire+ putte,
And Blancheflour ageyn him tytte.+
The kyng seyde, "Drery mote we be,
This routhe by thise children for-to see!"
The kyng that the ryng hadde
1025 For routhe of hem soon he radde,+
And at the amyral wyl he spede
The children from the deeth to lede.
"Sire," he seyde, "it is litel pris+
Thise children for-to slee, y-wis;

1007 **spille** destroy.
1010 **binne** within (that time).
1013 **bo** both.
1016 **swire** neck.
1017 **tire** pull back.
1019 **Wyth wrong** wrongfully. **i-lore** lost.
1020 **swire** neck.
1021 **tytte** drew, (?)exhorted.
1022 *we*, from Auch. MS., for 3e.
1025 **radde** spoke in counsel.
1028 **pris** value, worth.

1030   And it is wel more worshipe⁺
        Floris counseil that ye wite:
        Who him taughte that ilke gynne
        Thy tour for-to comen inne,
        And who him broghte ther,

1035   And other, that ye mowe be war."
        Than seyde the amyral, "As God me save,
        Floris shal his lyf have
        If he me telle who him taughte ther-to."
        [Than seyde the amyral to Floris tho,
        "Tel me who thee taughte hire to."]
        "That," seyde Floris, "shal I nevere do,
        [But if it be foryeve also
        That⁺ the gynne me taughte ther-to."]

1040   Now they bidden alle, y-wis,
        That the amyral graunte this—
        To foryeve that trespas
        If Floris tolde how it was.
        Now every word he hath him told,

1045   How that the mayde was for him sold;
        And how he was of Spayn a kynges sone
        For greet love thider i-come
        For-to fonde, wyth som gynne,
        That faire mayde for-to wynne;

1050   And how the porter was his man bicome
        For his gold and for his warisoun;
        And how he was in the floures bore.
        Alle the lordynges loughe⁺ ther-fore.

1030 **worshipe** honor.
1039 **That** (of) that (one who). After line 1038 something has been left
      out, and line 1039 is defective. The lines in brackets are thus
      supplied, and line 1039 emended, on the basis of the Auch. MS.
1041 *graunte* replaces *graunted*.
1053 **loughe** laughed.

Now the amyral—wel him tide!—
1055 Floris sette next his side,
And eft he made him stonde upright
And dubbed him ther knight,
And bad he sholde wyth him be
The forthermoste+ of his meynee.+
1060 Floris falleth doun to his feet
And preyeth yeve him his swete.
The amyral yaf him his lemman;
Alle that ther were thonkede him than.
To a chirche he lett hem brynge,+
1065 And dide hem wedde wyth a ryng.
Bothe thise two swete thynges, y-wis,
Felle his feet for-to kisse;
And thurgh counseil of Blancheflour,
Clarys was fet+ doun of the tour,
1070 And amyral wedded hire to quene.
Ther was feste swithe breme+—
I can not telle alle the sonde,+
But richer feste was nevere in londe.
Was it noght longe after than
1075 That to Floris tidyng cam
That the kyng his fader was deed.
The baronage yaf him reed+
That he sholde wende hom
And fonge+ his faire kyngdom.

1059 **forthermoste** foremost. **meynee** retinue.
1064 **lett hem brynge** had them brought.
1065 *dide hem wedde* for MS. *dede let wed hem.*
1069 **fet** fetched.
1071 **breme** glorious.
1072 **sonde** serving (of food).
1077 **reed** = *rede* counsel.
1079 **fonge** take.

138

1080   At the amyral they toke leve,
       And he biddeth hem bileve.+
       Hom he went wyth royal array,
       And was crouned wythin a short day.

1080–1083 The other versions have longer conclusions. In the Camb. MS. Floris gives wealth to those who have helped him before returning home, and the narrative ends with a perfunctory benediction. The Auch. MS. relates how the couple return home (after refusing the amyral's invitation to remain) and become Christian; there is also a perfunctory benediction.

1081 **bileve** remain.

Ywayn and Gawayn

Almyghty God that made mankynne,
He shilde his servauntes out of synne
And mayntene hem wyth myght and mayn
That herkne+ *Ywayn and Gawayn:*
5   They were knightes of the Table Rounde,
Ther-fore listneth a litel stounde!+
    Arthur the kyng of Englelond,
That wan al Wales wyth his hond
And al Scotland, as seyth the book
10 (And many more, if man wyl loke),
Of alle knightes he bar the pris:
In world was non so war and wys.
Trewe he was in al-kyn+ thyng,
As it bifel to swich a kyng.
15 He made a feste, the sooth to seye,
Upon the White-Sonneday,+
At Kerdyf, that is in Wales;
And after mete, ther in the halles,
Ful greet and gay was th' assemblee
20 Of lordes and ladies of that contree,
And als+ of knightes, war and wys,
And damyselles of muchel pris.
Echoon wyth other made greet gamen
And greet solas, as they were samen.+
25 Faste they carpede+ and curteisly

---

4 **herkne** hearken, listen to.
6 **a litel stounde** a short while.
13 **al-kyn** every kind of.
16 **White-Sonneday** Whitsunday.
21 **als** = *also*.
24 **samen** in company.
25 **carpede** conversed.

Of dedes of armes and venerye,+
And of gode knightes that lyvde than,
And how man myghte hem kyndely can+
By doughtinesse of her good dede
30 On ilke side, wher-som they yede;+
For they were stif+ in ilke stour,+
And ther-fore gete they greet honour.
They tolde of more trouthe hem bitwene
Thanne now among men heer is sene:
35 For trouthe and love is al bilaft.+
Men use now an other craft:
Wyth word men make it trewe and stable,
But in her feith is noght but fable;
Wyth the mouth men make it hale,+
40 But trewe trouthe is non in the tale.
Ther-fore heer-of now wyl I blynne.+
Of the Kyng Arthur I wyl bigynne,
And of his curteis companye.
Ther was the flour of chivalry!
45 Swich los+ they wonne wyth speres ord,+
Over al the world went the word!
    After mete went the kyng
Into chambre to slepyng,
And also went wyth him the quene.
50 That bihelde+ they al bidene,+
For they sawe hem nevere so
On heighe dayes to chambre go.

26 **venerye** hunting.
28 **can** know, recognize.
30 **yede** went.
31 **stif** bold. **stour** conflict.
35 **bilaft** = *bileft* left behind.
39 **hale** = *hol* sound.
41 **blynne** cease.
45 **los** fame. **ord** point.
50 **bihelde** noticed. **al bidene** at once.

But soon, whan they were went to slepe,
Knightes sete the dore to kepe:
55 Sir Dedyne and Sir Segramore,
Sir Gawayn and Sir Kay sete thor,+
And also sete ther Sir Ywayn,
And Colgrevaunce, of muchel mayn.
This knight that highte+ Colgrevaunce
60 Tolde his felawes of a chaunce+
And of a stour+ he hadde ben inne.
And al this tale herde the quene:
The chambre-dore she has unshet,+
And doun among hem she hire set.
65 Sodeynly she sat doun right
Er any of hem of hire hadde sight.
But Colgrevaunce ros up in hye+
And ther-of hadde Sir Kay envye
For he was of his tonge a skold+
70 And for-to boste he was ful bold.
"O, Colgrevaunce!" seyde Sir Kay,
"Ful light of lepes+ hast thou ben ay.
Thou wenest now that thee shal falle
For-to be hendest of us alle;
75 And the quene shal understonde
That heer is non so uncunnande.+
Al if thou rise and we sete stille,
We ne dide it for non ille,
Ne for no manere of feyntise,+

56 **thor** = *ther.*
59 **highte** was named.
60 **chaunce** incident, venture.
61 **stour** (armed) combat, contest.
63 **unshet** un-shut, opened.
67 **in hye** in haste.
69 **was of his tonge a skold** i.e., was abusive.
72 **light of lepes** i.e., ready at courtesies.
76 **uncunnande** unknowing (of manners).
79 **feyntise** indifference.

80   Ne us denyed noght for-to rise,
     That we ne hadde risen, hadde we hire seen."
     "Sire Kay, I wot wel," seyde the quene,
     "And it were good thou lefte swiche sawes,+
     And not despise so thy felawes."
85   "Madame," he seyde, "By Goddes doom,
     We ne wiste nothyng of thy coom.+
     And if we dide noght curteisly,
     Taketh to no vilanye,
     But preye ye now this gentil man
90   To telle the tale that he bigan."
     Colgrevaunce seyde to Sir Kay,
     "By grete God, that oweth this day,
     No more meneth me thy flyte+
     Thanne it were a flyes bite.
95   Ful ofte wel bettre men thanne I
     Hast thou despised despiteously.+
     It is ful seemly, as me thynke,+
     A brok+ among men for-to stynke.
     So it fareth by thee, Sire Kay:
100   Of wikked wordes hast thou ben ay.
     And sith thy wordes ben wikked and felle,
     This tyme ther-to namore I telle
     But of the thyng that I bigan."
     And soon Sir Kay him answerde than,
105   And seyde ful tite+ to the quene,
     "Madame, if ye hadde noght heer ben,
     We sholde have herd a sely+ cas;
     Now lette ye us of oure solas.

83 **sawes** talk, sayings.
86 **coom** coming.
93 **flyte** (scolding) attack.
96 **despiteously** spitefully.
97 **me thynke** = *me thynketh* (it) seems (to) me.
98 **brok** badger.
105 **tite** quickly.
107 **sely** strange, curious.

Ther-fore, Madame, we wolde you preye
110   That ye comaunde him to seye
And telle forth, as he hadde tyght."+
Than answerde that hende knight,
"My lady is so avysee+
That she wyl noght comaunde me
115   To telle that toucheth me to ille.+
She is noght of so wikked wylle."
Sir Kay seyde than ful smertly,
"Madame, al-hol this+ companye
Preyeth you hertely, now a-melle,+
120   That he his tale forth myghte telle.
If ye wol noght for oure preying,
For feith ye owe unto the kyng,
Comaundeth him his tale to telle,
That we mowe here how it bifelle."
125   Than seyde the quene, "Sire Colgrevaunce,
I preye thee, tak no grevaunce
This kene carpyng of Sir Kay;
Of wikked wordes hath he ben ay,
So that non may him chastise.
130   Ther-fore I preye thee, on al wyse,+
That thou lette noght for his sawes
To telle to me and thy felawes
Al thy tale, how it bitidde:
For my love I thee preye and bidde."
135   "Certes, Madame, that is me loth;
But for I wyl noght make you wroth,

111 **tyght** intended.
113 **avysee** considerate, discreet.
115 **to ille** dishonorably.
118 **al-hol this** this entire.
119 **a-melle** together.
130 **on al wyse** by all means.
132 *To* for MS. *At,* here and subsequently.

Youre comaundement I shal fulfille
If ye wol listnen me untille.+
Wyth hertes and eres understondes,+
140 And I shal telle you swiche tithandes+
That ye herde nevere non swiche
Reherced in no kyngesriche.+
But word fareth as doth the wynd
But if+ men it in herte bynde;
145 And word whoso trewely taketh
By the eres into the herte it goth;
And in the herte ther is the hord+
And knowyng of ech mannes word.
Herkneth, hende, unto my spelle:
150 Trufles+ shal I you non telle,
Ne lesynges+ for-to gere you lawe;+
But I shal seye right as I saw.

Now as this tyme sixe yere
I rod allone, as ye shulle here,
155 Aboute for-to seche aventures,
Wel armed in gode armures.
In a frith+ I fond a strete+
Ful thik and hard, I you bihete,
Wyth thornes, breres, and many a whinne;+
160 Neer-hond alday I rod ther-inne,
And thurgh I passed wyth muchel peyne.

138 **untille** unto, to.
139 **understondes** = *understondeth.*
140 **tithandes** = *tidynges.*
142 **kyngesriche** realm.
144 **But if** unless.
147 **hord** hoard.
150 **Trufles** trifles.
151 **lesynges** lies. **gere you lawe** cause you (to) laugh.
157 **frith** woodland. **strete** path.
159 **whinne** prickly shrub.

Than cam I soon into a playne
Wher I gan see a brettis+ brod,
And thiderward ful faste I rod.
165 I saw the walles and the dike,+
And hertely wel it gan me like;
And on the draw-brigge saw I stonde
A knight wyth faucon on his honde.
This ilke knight, that be ye bold,+
170 Was lord and keper of that hold.+
I halsed+ him kyndely as I couthe;
He answerde me myldely wyth mouthe;
My styrop took that hende knight,
And kyndely comaunded me to light.
175 His comaundement I dide anane,+
And into halle soon were we tane.+
He thonked God, that gode man, .
Sevene sithes er evere he blan,+
And the weye that me thider broghte
180 And als the auntures that I soghte.
Thus wente we inne–God do him mede!–
And in his honde he ledde my stede.
Whan we were in that faire paleys
(It was ful worthly wroght alweys),
185 I saw no man of moder born.
But a bord heng us biforn,
Was nother of iren ne of tree,
Ne I wiste wher-of it myghte be;

163 **brettis** brattice.
165 **dike** ditch, moat.
169 **bold** assured.
170 **hold** stronghold.
171 **halsed** greeted.
175 **anane** = *anon.*
176 **tane** = *taken.*
178 **blan** ceased.

And by that bord ther heng a mal;⁺

190   The knight smot on ther wythal
Thries, and by than myghte man see
Bifore him come a faire meynee,
Curteis men in word and dede.
To stable soon they ladde my stede.

195   A damysel cam unto me,
The seemlieste that evere I see—
Lufsomer lyvde nevere in londe.
Hendely she took me by the honde,
And soon that gentil creature

200   Al unlaced myn armure.
Into a chambre she me ledde,
And wyth a mantel she me cledde:⁺
It was of purpre,⁺ faire and fyne,
And the pane⁺ of riche ermine.

205   Alle the folk were went us fro,
And ther was non than but we two.
She served me hendely⁺ to hende:⁺
Hir maneres myghte no man amende;
Of tonge she was trewe and renable,⁺

210   And of hir semblaunt softe and stable.⁺
Ful fayn I wolde, if that I myghte,
Have woned wyth that swete wighte.
And whan we sholde go to soupere,
That lady wyth a lufsom chere

215   Ledde me doun into the halle.
Ther were we servde wel at alle.

189 **mal** hammer. *ther* is supplied.
202 **cledde** clad.
203 **purpre** purple cloth.
204 **pane** lining.
207 **hendely** graciously. **to hend** = *to honde* (here, a rhyme tag).
209 **renable** ready, fluent.
210 **stable** steadfast.

It nedeth noght to telle the mes,+
For wonder wel were we at ese.
Bifore me sat the lady brighte
220 Curteisly my mete to dighte.+
Us wontede nother baken+ ne rost.
And after soupere, seyde myn hoste
That he coude noght tell the day
That any knight er wyth him lay,
225 Or that any auntures soghte.
Ther-fore he preyde me, if he moghte,+
On alle wyse, whan I come ageyn,
That I sholde come to him certeyn.
I seyde, "Sire, gladly, if I may."
230 It hadde ben shame have I seyde him nay.
That nyght hadde I ful good reste,
And my stede esed of the beste.

As soon as it was dayes light,
Forth to fare soon I was dight.
235 My leve of myn hoste took I thore+
And went my weye wythouten more,
Auntures for-to layte+ in lond.
A faire forest soon I fond.
Me thoghte my hap ther fel ful hard,
240 For ther was many a wilde leopard,
Leouns, beres, bothe bul and bor,
That rewefully gan rope and rore.+
Awey I drough me, and wyth that,

217 **mes** mess, food.
220 **dighte** make ready.
221 **baken** baked meats.
226 **moghte** = *myghte.*
235 **thore** = *ther.*
237 **layte** search for.
242 **rope and rore** i.e., make an uproar.

I saw soon wher a man sat
245 On a launde,+ the fouleste wight
That evere yet man saw in sight;
He was a lothly creature,
For foule he was out of mesure;
A wonder mace in honde he hadde.
250 And soon my weye to him I made.
His heed me thoghte was so greet
As of a rouncy or a neet;+
Unto his belt heng his hare.+
And after that biheeld I mare:+
255 To his fore-heed biheeld I than—
Was brodder thanne two large span;
He hadde eres as an olifaunt,
And was wel more+ thanne geaunt;
His face was ful brod and flat,
260 His nose was cutted as a cat;
His browes were like litel buskes+
And his teeth like bore-tuskes;
A ful greet bulge upon his bak:
Ther was noght made wythouten lak+—
265 His chin was fast unto his breste.
On his mace he gan him reste.
Also it was a wonder wede+
That the cherl inne yede;
Nother of wolle ne of linne+
270 Was the wede that he went inne.

245 **launde** grassy space.
252 **rouncy or a neet** carthorse or an ox.
253 **hare** = *heer* hair.
254 **mare** = *more*.
258 **wel more** i.e., larger.
261 **buskes** bushes.
264 **lak** fault.
267 **wede** garment.
269 **linne** linen.

Whan he me saw, he stood uprighte;
I frayned+ him if he wolde fighte,
For ther-to was I in good wylle.
But as a beste than stood he stille.
275   I hoped that he no wyttes couthe,
No resoun for-to speke wyth mouthe.
To him I spak ful hardily,
And seyde, "What artow, belamy?"+
He seyde ageyn, "I am a man."
280   I seyde, "Swich saw I nevere non."
"What artow?" al-soon+ seyde he.
I seyde, "Swich as thou heer may see."
I seyde, "What dost thou heer allone?"
He seyde, "I kepe this bestes echone."+
285   I seyde, "That is merveil, think'th me;
For I herde nevere of man but thee,
In wildernesse ne in forestes,
That kepyng hadde of wilde bestes,
But they were bounde faste in hold."
290   He seyde, "Of thise is non so bold,
Nother by day ne by nyght,
Ones to passe out of my sight."
I seyde, "How so? Tel me thy skile."
"Parfay," he seyde, "gladly I wyl."
295   He seyde, "In al this faire foreste
Is ther non so wilde beste
That remuwe+ dar, but stille stonde
Whan I am to him comande.+
And ay whan that I wyl him fonge+

272 **frayned** inquired (of).
278 **belamy** fair friend.
281 **al-soon** straightway.
284 **echone** = *echoon.*
297 **remuwe** move away, stir.
298 **comande** = *comynge.*
299 **fonge** seize.

300 Wyth my fyngres, that ben stronge,
    I gere him crie⁺ on swich manere
    That alle the bestes, whan they him here,
    Aboute me than come they alle
    And to my feet faste they falle,
305 On her manere mercy to crie.
    But understond now redily,
    Alyve is ther lyvynge no mo
    But I that durste among hem go,
    That he ne sholde soon be to-rent.⁺
310 But they ben at my comaundement:
    To me they come whan I hem calle,
    And I am maister of hem alle."
    Than he axed anon-right,
    What man I was. I seyde, a knight
315 That soughte auntures in that londe,
    "My body to assaye and fonde.
    And I thee preye, of thy counseil
    Thou teche me to som merveil."
    He seyde, "I can no wonders telle;
320 But heer-biside is a welle:
    Wend thider and do as I seye—
    Thou passest noght al quit aweye.⁺
    Folwe forth this ilke strete
    And soon som merveiles shaltow mete.
325 The welle is under the faireste tree
    That evere was in this contree;
    By that welle hongeth a basin
    That is of gold good and fyne,
    Wyth a chayne, trewely to telle,
330 That wyl reche into the welle;
    Ther is a chapel neer ther-by

301 **gere him crie** cause him (to) cry.
309 **to-rent** torn to pieces.
322 **al quit aweye** i.e., freely, without having paid something.

That noble is and ful lufly.
By the welle stondeth a ston;
Tak the basin soon anon,
335 And cast on water wyth thyn honde,
And soon thou shalt see newe tithande.+
A storm shal rise, and a tempeste,
Al aboute, by este and weste;
Thou shalt here many thonder-blast
340 Al aboute thee blowynge faste;
And ther shal come swich sleet and reyn,
That unethes+ shaltow stonde ageyn;
Of lightnesse shaltow see a lowe,+
Unethes thou shalt thyselve knowe;
345 And if thou passe wythoute grevaunce,
Than hastow the faireste chaunce
That evere yet hadde any knight
That thider cam to kythe+ his myght."

Than took I leve and went my weye,
350 And rod unto the mydde-day.
By-than I cam wher I sholde be,
I saw the chapel and the tree.
Ther I fond the faireste thorn
That evere grewe sith God was born:
355 So thik it was wyth leves grene,
Myghte no reyn come bitwene;
And that grenenesse lasteth ay,
For no wynter dere+ it may.
I fond the basin, as he tolde,
360 And the welle wyth water cold.

---

336 **tithande** = *tidyng*(es).
342 **unethes** hardly.
343 **lowe** blaze, flash.
348 **kythe** make known.
358 **dere** harm.

An emeraude+ was the ston—
Richer saw I nevere non—
On foure rubees on hight+ stondande;+
Her light lasted+ over al the londe.
365 And whan I saw that seemly sight,
It made me bothe joyeful and light.
I took the basin soon anon
And helded+ water upon the ston.
The weder wex than wonder blak
370 And the thonder faste gan crake;
Ther come swiche stormes of hayl and reyn,
Unethes I myghte stonde ther-ageyn.
The store+ wyndes blewe ful loude—
So kene come nevere er of cloude.
375 I was dryven wyth snow and sleet,
Unethes I myghte stonde on my feet;
In my face the levenyng+ smot,
I wende have brent,+ so was it hot.
That weder made me so wyl of rede,+
380 I hoped soon to have my dede;+
And certes, if it longe hadde last,
I hope I hadde nevere thennes past.+
But thurgh His myght that tholed+ wounde,
The storm cessed wythin a stounde;
385 Than wex the weder faire ageyn,

361 **emeraude** emerald.
363 **on hight** on high. **stondande** = *stondynge*.
364 **lasted** extended.
368 **helded** poured out.
373 **store** mighty, fierce.
377 **levenyng** lightning.
378 **I wende have brent** I expected to have (been) burned.
379 **so wyl of rede** i.e., at a loss for what to do.
380 **dede** = *deeth*.
382 **past** = *passed*.
383 **tholed** suffered.

And ther-of was I wonder fayn,
For best confort of alle thyng
Is solas after myslikyng.+
Than saw I soon a myrie sight:
390 Of alle the foweles that ben in flyght
Lightede so thikke upon that tree
That bough ne leef non myghte I see.
So myrily than gonne they synge
That al the wode bigan to rynge;
395 Ful myrie was the melodye
Of her song and of her crie:
Ther herde nevere man non swilke,+
But if any hadde herd that ilke.
And whan that myrie dyn was don,
400 An other noise than herde I soon,
As it were of horsmen
More thanne other nyen or ten.
  Soon than saw I come a knight,
In riche armure was he dight;
405 And soon whan I gan on him loke,
My sheeld and spere to me I took.
That knight to me hyed ful faste,
And kene wordes out gan he caste:
He bad that I sholde telle him tite
410 Why I dide him swich despite,
Wyth wedres wakened him of reste
And don him wrong in his foreste;
"Ther-fore," he seyde, "thou shalt abeye."+
And wyth that cam he egrely,+
415 And seyde, I hadde ayeins resoun
Don him greet destruccioun,

388 **myslikyng** (something) displeasing.
397 **swilke** = *swiche*.
413 **abeye** pay for.
414 **egrely** fiercely.

154

And myghte it nevere more amende;
Ther-fore he bad I sholde me fende.+
And soon I smot him on the shelde;
420 My shaft brak out in the felde;
And than he bar me soon by strengthe
Out of my sadel my speres lengthe.
I wot that he was largely
By the shuldres more thanne I;+
425 And by the deeth that I shal thole,+
My stede by his was but a fole.+
For mat+ I lay doun on the grounde,
So was I stonyed+ in that stounde.
A word to me wolde he noght seye,
430 But took my stede and wente aweye.
Ful sorily than ther I sat,
For wo I wiste noght what was what.
Wyth my stede he went in hy
The same weye that he cam by;
435 And I durste folwe him no ferre
For doute me sholde biteo werre.+
And also yet, by Goddes doom,
I ne wiste wher he bicam.
    Than I thoghte how I hadde hight+
440 Unto myn hoste, the hende knight,
And also to his lady brighte,
To come ageyn, if that I myghte.
Myn armures left I ther echoon,

418 **fende** defend.
424 **By the shuldres more thanne I** i.e., a head taller.
425 **And by the deeth that I shal thole** i.e., surely.
426 **fole** foal.
427 **mat** defeated, exhausted.
428 **stonyed** stunned.
436 **For doute me sholde biteo werre** for fear that I should bring worse on myself.
439 **hight** promised.

For elles myghte I noght have gon.
445 Unto myn inn I cam by day;
The hende knight and the faire may
Of my coom+ were they ful glade,
And noble semblaunt they me made;
In alle thynges they have hem born
450 As they dide the nyght biforn.
Soon they wiste wher I hadde ben,
And seyde that they hadde nevere seen
Knight that evere thider cam
Take the weye ageyn hom.
455 On this wyse that tyme I wroghte:
I fond the folyes that I soghte."

"Now sikerly," seyde Sir Ywayn,
"Thou art my cosin-germain;+
Trewe love sholde be us bitwene,
460 As sholde bitwixe brether+ ben.
Thou art a fool that thou ne hadde are+
Told me of this ferly fare;+
For certes I sholde anon-right
Have venged thee of that ilke knight.
465 So shal I yet, if that I may."
And than as smertly seyde Sir Kay—
He carped to hem wordes grete:
"It is sene, now is after mete:
More boste is in a pot of wyne
470 Thanne in a carkeis of Seint Martyne.+
Arme thee smertly, Sir Ywayn,

447 **coom** coming.
458 **cosin-germain** close kinsman.
460 **brether** brothers.
461 **are** = *er* before.
462 **ferly fare** wondrous venture.
470 **a carkeis of Seint Martyne** i.e., a flitch of beef.

And soon, that thou were come ageyn;
Loke thou fille wel thy panel+
And in thy sadel set thou wel;
475 And whan thou wendest, I thee preye,
A baner wel that thou desplaye;
And, rede I, er thou wende,
Thou tak thy leve at ilke frende:
And if it so bitide this nyght
480 That thee in sleep drecche+ any wight,
Or any dremes make thee rad,+
Turn ageyn and sey I bad."+
    The quene answerde wyth mylde mood
And seyde, "Sire Kay, artow wood?+
485 What the devil is thee wythinne
That thy tonge may nevere blynne+
Thy felawes so fouly to shende?+
Certes, Sire Kay, thou art unhende.
By Him that for us suffred pyne,
490 Sire, and thy tonge were myn,
I sholde bicalle it tite of tresoun;+
And so myghte thou do, by good resoun:
Thy tonge doth thee greet dishonour,
And ther-fore is it thy traitour."
495 And than al-soon Sir Ywayn
Ful hendely answerde ageyn
(Al if men seyde him vilanye,
He carped ay ful curteisly):
"Madame," he seyde unto the quene,

---

473 **panel** saddlecloth.
480 **drecche** troubles.
481 **rad** afraid.
482 **bad** foretold (it).
484 **wood** mad.
486 **blynne** cease.
487 **shende** harm, scold.
491 **bicalle it tite of tresoun** accuse it at once of treason.

500   "Ther sholde no strif be us bitwene.
     Uncouth men wel may he shende
     That to his felawes is so unhende.
     And as, Madame, man seyth certeyn
     That whoso flyteth⁺ or turneth ageyn,
505   He bigynneth al the melee,⁺
     So wyl I noght it fare⁺ by me.
     Lete him seye hoolly his thoght—
     His wordes greve me right noght."
       As they were in this spekyng,
510   Out of the chambre cam the kyng;
     The barouns that were ther, certeyn,
     Smertly rise they him ageyn.
     He bad hem sitte doun al bidene,
     And doun he sat him by the quene.
515   The quene tolde him faire and wel,
     As she couthe, everich a deel⁺
     Ful apertly al the chaunce
     As it bifel Sir Colgrevaunce.
     Whan she hadde told him how it ferde,
520   And the kyng hir tale hadde herd,
     He swor by his owene croune
     And his fadres soule, Uterpendragoune,
     That he sholde see that ilke sight
     By that day thennes a fourtenyght,
525   On Seint Johnes even, the Baptist,
     That beste bern⁺ was under⁺ Crist.
     "Swithe,"⁺ he seyde, "wend wyth me,
     Whoso wyl that wonder see."

504 **flyteth** reproaches.
505 **melee** fight.
506 **fare** come about.
516 **everich a deel** entirely.
526 **bern** man. **under** after.
527 **Swithe** quickly.

The kynges word myghte noght be hidd:
530 Over al the court soon it was kidd,+
And ther was non so litel page
That he ne was fayn+ of that viage;+
And knightes and squiers were ful fayn:
Mysliked non but Sir Ywayn.
535 To himself he made greet mone,
For he wolde have went allone;
In herte he hadde greet myslikyng
For the wendyng of the kyng,
Al for he hoped, wythouten faile,
540 That Sir Kay sholde aske the bataile,
Or elles Sir Gawayn, knight vaylaunt,
And other wolde the kyng it graunte:
Whoso it wolde first crave+
Of hem two soon myghte it have.
545 The kynges wyl wolde he noght abide,
Worthe of+ him what may bitide:
By him allone he thoghte to wende
And take the grace that God wolde sende.
He thoghte to be wel on his weye
550 Er it were passed the thridde day,
And to assaye if he myghte mete
Wyth that ilke narwe strete,
Wyth thornes and wyth breres sette+
That mennes weye myghte lightly lette,+
555 And also for-to fynde the hold
That Sir Colgrevaunce of tolde,
The knight and the mayden eke;

530 **kidd** made known.
532 **fayn** glad. **viage** journey.
542 *it* is supplied.
543 **crave** ask (for).
546 **Worthe of** become, happen (to).
553 **sette** = *set*.
554 **lightly lette** easily hinder.

The forest faste than wolde he seche,
And als the carl of Caymes kyn,+
560 And the wilde bestes wyth him—
The tree wyth briddes+ ther-upon—
The chapel, the basin, and the ston.
His thoght wolde he telle to no frende
Until he wiste how it wolde ende.

565 Than wente Ywayn to his inn;+
His men he fond redy there-inne.
Unto a squier gan he seye,
"Go swithe and sadel my palfrey,
And so thou do my stronge stede,
570 And tak wyth thee my beste wede;
At yon yate I wyl out ride.
Wythouten toun I shal thee bide,
And hy thou smertly unto me,
For I moot maken a journee.

575 Ageyn shalt thou brynge my palfrey.
And I forbede thee oght to seye.
If thou wylt any more me see,
Lat non wite of my privetee;
And if any man thee oght frayne,+
580 Loke now lely+ that thou layne."+
"Sire," he seyde, "wyth ful good wylle,
As ye bidde, I shal fulfille.
At youre owene wyl mowe ye ride:
For me ye shulle noght be ascried."+

---

559 **carl of Caymes kyn** churl of the race of Cain. Tradition had it that
monsters, giants, evil spirits, and the like were descendants of Cain.
561 **briddes** birds.
565 **inn** lodging.
576 *I* is supplied.
579 **frayne** inquire (of).
580 **lely** faithfully. **layne** conceal (it).
584 **ascried** discovered.

585　　Forth than wente Sir Ywayn:
　　　He thenketh, er he come ageyn,
　　　To wreke+ his cosin at his myght.
　　　The squier hath his harneys+ dight;
　　　He dide right as his maister radde:+
590　His stede, his armures he him ladde.+
　　　Whan Ywayn was wythouten toun,
　　　On his palfrey lighted he doun
　　　And dighte him right wel in his wede,
　　　And leep upon his gode stede.
595　Forth he rod anon-right
　　　Until it neighed nere the nyght.
　　　He passed many a heighe mountayne
　　　In wildernesse, and many a playne,
　　　Til he cam to that lither sty+
600　That him bihoved passe by.
　　　Than was he siker for-to see
　　　The welle and the faire tree;
　　　The castel saw he at the laste,
　　　And thider hyed he ful faste.
605　More curteisye and more honour
　　　Fond he wyth hem in that tour,
　　　And more confort by many fold
　　　Thanne Colgrevaunce hadde him of told.
　　　That nyght was he herberd+ ther–
610　So wel was he nevere er.
　　　　　At morne he went forth by the strete,
　　　And wyth the cherl soon gan he mete
　　　That sholde telle to him the weye.

587 **wreke** avenge.
588 **harneys** armor, equipment.
589 **radde** advised.
590 **ladde** = *ledde*.
599 **lither sty** evil, ugly path.
609 **herberd** harbored.

He signed him,[+] the sooth to seye,

615 Twenty sith[+] er evere he blan,
Swich merveil hadde he of that man;
For he hadde wonder that nature
Myghte make so foul a creature.
Than to the welle he rod, gode pase,[+]

620 And doun he lighted in that place,
And soon the basin he hath tane
And cast the water upon the stane;[+]
And soon ther wexe, wythouten faile,
Wynd and thonder, reyn and hayl.

625 Whan it was cessed, than saw he
The foweles lighte upon the tree;
They songe ful faire upon that thorn
Right as they hadde don biforn.
And soon he saw comynge a knight

630 As faste so the fowel in flyght,
Wyth rude[+] semblaunt and sterne chere;
And hastily he neighed nere.
To speke of love no tyme was thare,[+]
For either hated other ful sare;[+]

635 Togidre smertly gan they dryve;
Her sheldes soon bigan to rive;[+]
Her shaftes shivrede to her hande,[+]
But they were bothe ful wel sittande.[+]
Out they drowe her swerdes kene

---

614 **signed him** i.e., made the sign of the cross.
615 **sith** times.
619 **gode pase** i.e., rapidly.
622 **stane** = *ston(e)*.
631 **rude** rough.
633 **thare** = *ther*.
634 **sare** = *sore*.
636 **rive** shiver, shatter.
637 **hande** = *honde(s)*.
638 **sittande** = *sittynge*.

162

640 And delte strokes hem bitwene;
Al to peces they hewede her sheldes—
The colpons+ flowe out in the feldes;
On helmes strike they so wyth ire,
At ilke strok out brast the fyr.
645 Either of hem gode buffets bede,+
And nother wolde stire of the stede;
Ful kenely they kidde+ her myght,
And feynde hem noght+ for-to fighte,
At her hauberkes,+ that men myghte kenne,
650 The blood out of her bodies renne;+
Either on other leyde so faste,
The bataile myghte noght longe laste.
Hauberkes ben broken and helmes riven,
Stiffe strokes were ther yeven.
655 They foghte on hors stifly alweys;
The bataile was wel more to preise.+
But atte laste Sir Ywayn
On his felawe kidde his mayn:+
So egrely he smot him than,
660 He clefte the helm and the hern-pan.+

The knight wiste he was nere dede:
To flee than was his beste rede;
And faste he fledde, wyth al his mayn,

642 **colpons** cuttings, bits.
645 **bede** offered.
647 **kidde** made known.
648 **feynde ... noght** didn't (merely) pretend.
649 **hauberkes** (coats of) chain mail.
650 **renne** = *ran*.
656 **wel more to preise** i.e., much more worth praising. The English translator has omitted the fact upon which this line is based: that both men were careful not to strike or harm the horses.
658 **kidde his mayn** showed his might.
660 **hern-pan** skull.

And faste folwed Sir Ywayn.
665 But he ne myghte him overtake,
Ther-fore greet murnyng gan he make;
He folwed him ful stoutelik+
And wolde have tane him, deed or quik.
He folwed him to the citee;
670 No man lyvynge mette he.
Whan they come to the castel yate,
In he folwed faste ther-at.
At either entree was, y-wis,
Streytly wroght a porte-colys+
675 Shod wel wyth iren and steel,
And also grounden+ wonder wel;
Under that than was a swike+
That made Sir Ywayn to myslike:
Whan his hors foot touched ther-on,
680 Than fel the porte-colys anon
Bitwixe him and his hinder-arsoun:+
Thurgh sadel and stede it smot al doun.
His spores+ of his heles it shar;+
Than hadde Ywayn murnyng mare.+
685 But as he wende have passed quite,+
Than fel that other bifore, as tite.
A faire grace yet fel him so,
Al if it smot his hors in two
And his spores of either hele
690 That himself passed so wel!

667 **stoutelik** stoutly, fiercely.
674 **porte-colys** portcullis.
676 **grounden** ground (sharp).
677 **swike** trap.
679 *Whan* is supplied.
681 **hinder-arsoun** back part of the saddle.
683 **spores** spurs. **shar** sheared.
684 **mare** = *more*.
685 **wende have passed quite** expected (to) have passed freely.

Bitwene the yates now is he tane,
Ther-fore he maketh ful muchel mane;+
And muchel murnyng gan he ma+
For the knight was went him fra.+

695 As he was stoken in that stalle+
He herde bihynde him in a walle
A dore opened, faire and wel,
And ther-out cam a damysel.
After hire the dore she stak;+

700 Ful hende wordes to him she spak:
"Sire," she seyde, "by Seint Myghel,
Heer thou hast a feble hostel!+
Thou mon be deed, is noght at layn,+
For my lord that thou hast slayn.

705 Siker it is that thou him slough;
My lady maketh sorwe ynough,
And al his meynee everichoon.
Ther hastow fomen+ many oon;
To be thy bane+ ben they ful bold.

710 Thou brekest noght out of this hold;
And for they waite,+ they mowe noght fayle:
They wol thee slee in playn bataile."
He seyde, "They ne shulle, so God me rede,
For al her myght, do me to dede,+

692 **mane** = *mone* complaint.
693 **ma** = *make*.
694 **fra** = *fro(m)*.
695 **stoken in that stalle** closed in that place.
699 **stak** closed, shut.
702 **feble hostel** poor hostelry.
703 **Thou mon be deed, is noght at layn** i.e., you must die—it cannot be concealed.
708 **fomen** foemen.
709 **bane** (dealers of) death.
711 **waite** lie in wait (for).
714 **dede** = *deeth*.

715 Ne no hondes upon me leye!"
  She seyde, "No, certes, if I may!
  Al if thou be heer streytly stad,⁺
  Me thinketh thou are noght ful adrad;⁺
  And Sire," she seyde, "on alle wyse,
720 I owe thee honour and servise.
  I was in message at⁺ the kyng
  Bifore this tyme, whil I was ying;⁺
  I was noght than so avysee⁺
  As a damysel oghte to be.
725 From the tyme that I was light,⁺
  In court was non so hende knight
  That unto me than wolde take hede
  But thou allone, God do thee mede!
  Greet honour thou dide to me,
730 And that shal I now quite⁺ thee.
  I wot, if thou be selde seen,
  Thou art the kyng sone Urien,
  And thy name is Sir Ywayn.
  Of me mayst thou be certeyn:
735 If thou wylt my counseil leve,⁺
  Thou shalt fynde no man thee to greve.
  I shal lene⁺ thee heer my ryng,
  But yeld it⁺ me at myn axyng:
  Whan thou art broght of al thy peyne,

717 **streytly stad** sorely bestead, situated.
718 **adrad** afraid.
721 **in message at** on a mission to.
722 **ying** = *yong.*
723 **avysee** observant, discreet.
725 **was light** alighted, i.e., arrived.
730 **quite** requite.
735 **leve** believe.
737 **lene** give.
738 **yeld it** give it back (to).

740 Yeld it than to me ageyn.
  As the bark hyleth+ the tree,
  Right so shal my ryng do thee.
  Whan thou in honde hast the ston,
  Dere+ shulle they do thee non;
745 For the ston is of swich myght,
  Of thee shulle men have no sight."
  Wite ye wel that Sir Ywayn
  Of thise wordes was ful fayn.
  In at the dore she him ledde
750 And dide him sitte upon hir bedde.
  A quylt ful noble lay ther-on—
  Richer saw he nevere non.
  She seyde if he wolde any thyng,
  He sholde be served at his likyng.
755 He seyde that ete wolde he fayn;
  She wente and cam ful soon ageyn.
  A capon rosted broghte she soon,
  A clene cloth and breed ther-on,
  And a pot wyth riche wyne,
760 And a pece+ to fille it inne.
  He eet and drank wyth ful good chere,
  For ther-of hadde he greet mystere.+
   Whan he hadde eten and dronken wel,
  Greet noise he herde in the castel:
765 They soghte over-al him to have slayn—
  To venge her lord were they ful bayn,+
  Er that the cors+ in erthe was leyd.

741 **hyleth** hides, covers.
744 **Dere** harm, injury.
760 **pece** (wine) cup.
762 **mystere** need.
766 **bayn** eager.
767 **cors** corpse, body.

The damysel soon to him seyde,
"Now seche they thee faste for-to slo.⁺

770 But whoso evere come or go,
Be thou nevere the more adrede,
Ne stire thou noght out of this stede;
In this heer⁺ seche they wylle,
But on this bed loke thou be stille:

775 Of hem alle mak thou no fors.⁺
But whan that they shulle bere the cors
Unto the chirche for-to burye,
Than shaltow here a sory cry,
So shulle they make a dolful dyn.

780 Than shulle they seche thee eft heer-in;
But loke thou be of herte light,
For of thee shulle they have no sight.
Heer shaltow be, maugree her berd;⁺
And ther-fore be thou noght aferd:

785 Thy fomen shulle be as the blynde;
Bothe bifore thee and bihynde,
On ilke side shaltow be soght.
Now moot I go; but dreed thee noght,
For I shal do that thee is leef,

790 If al it turne me to myschief."
Whan she cam unto the yate,
Ful many men fond she ther-at
Wel armed, and wolde ful fayn
Have taken and slayn Sir Ywayn.

795 Half his stede ther founde they,
That wythinne the yates lay;
But the knight ther founde they noght:

---

769 **slo** = *slee.*
773 **this heer** i.e., this place.
775 **mak . . . no fors** pay no attention.
783 **maugree her berd** in spite of their beard(s), i.e., in spite of anything they can do.

Than was her muchel sorwe unsoght.+
Dore ne wyndow was ther non
800 Wher he myghte awey gon.
They seyde he sholde ther be laft+
Or elles he couthe of wicchecraft,
Or he couthe nygromancye,+
Or he hadde wynges for-to flye.
805   Hastily than wente they alle
And soghte him in the maydens halle,
In chambres heighe, is noght to hide,
And in solers+ on ilke side.
Sir Ywayn saw ful wel al that,
810 And stille upon the bed he sat.
Ther was non that ones mynte+
Unto the bed to smyte a dynt.
Al aboute they smyte so faste
That many of her wepens braste.
815 Muchel sorwe they made ilkane+
For they ne myghte wreke her lordes bane.+
They wente awey wyth drery chere,
And soon ther-after come the bere,+
A lady folwed, white as milk—
820 In al that londe was non swilk.+
She wrang hir fyngres—out brast the blood;
For muchel wo she was nere wood.
Hir faire heer she al to-drough,+

798 **unsoght** (?) manifest, (?) immeasurable.
801 **laft** = *left*.
803 **nygromancye** necromancy.
808 **solers** upper rooms.
811 **mynte** thought, (?) aimed (a stroke).
815 **ilkane** = *echoon*.
816 **bane** death.
818 **bere** bier.
820 **swilk** = *swich*.
823 **al to-drough** i.e., pulled at violently.

And ful ofte fel she doun in swough; +
825   She wepte wyth a ful drery vois.
The holy water and the crois +
Was born bifore the processioun;
Ther folwede many a moder sone;
Bifore the cors rod a knight
830   On his stede, that was ful wight, +
In his armures wel arrayed,
Wyth spere and targe + goodly grayed. +
Than Sir Ywayn herde the cry
And the dol of that faire lady;
835   For more sorwe myghte non have
Thanne she hadde whan he went to grave.
Prestes and monkes on her wyse
Ful solempnily dide the servise.
   Als Lunete ther stood in the thronge,
840   Until Sir Ywayn thoghte hire longe. +
Out of the throng the weye she tase; +
Unto Sir Ywayn faste she gase. +
She seyde, "Sire, how artow stad? +
I hope ful wel thou hast ben rad." +
845   "Certes," he seyde, "Thou seyst wel ther!
So abayst + was I nevere er."
He seyde, "Lemman, I preye thee,
If it any wyse may be,

---

824 **swough** (a) swoon.
826 **crois** = *cros.*
830 **wight** strong.
832 **targe** shield. **grayed** prepared, adorned.
840 **longe** long (away).
841 **tase** = *taketh.*
842 **gase** = *goth.*
843 **how artow stad** i.e., how are you getting on?
844 **I hope ful wel thou hast ben rad** I fully expect that you have been frightened.
846 **abayst** disconcerted.

That I myghte loke a litel throwe+
850 Out at som hole or som wyndow;
For wonder fayn," he seyde, "wolde I
Have a sight of the lady.
The mayden than ful soon unshet+
In a place a privy wiket;
855 Ther of the lady he hadde a sight.
Loude she cried to God Almyght:
"Of his synnes do him pardoun!
For certeynly in no regioun
Was nevere knight of his beautee,
860 Ne after him shal nevere non be;
In al the world, from ende to ende,
Is non so curteis ne so hende.
God graunte the grace thou may wone+
In hevene, wyth His owene Sone!
865 For so large+ lyveth non in lede,+
Ne non so doughty of good dede!"
Whan she hadde thus made hir spel+
In swonyng ful oft-sithes she fel.

Now lete we the lady be,
870 And of Sir Ywayn speke we.
Love, that is so muchel of mayn,
Sore hadde wounded Sir Ywayn,
That wher-so he shal ride or go,
His herte she hath, that is his fo;
875 His herte he hath set al bidene
Wher himself dar noght be sene.
But thus in longyng bideth he

849 **throwe** time.
853 **unshet** un-shut, opened.
863 **wone** dwell.
865 **large** liberal. **in lede** on earth.
867 **spel** speech.

And hopeth that it shal bettre be.
Alle that were at the enterement+
880 Toke her leve at the lady gent,
And hom now ben they hoolly gon,
And the lady left allone,
Dwellynge wyth hir chamberere+
And other more that were hire dere.
885 Than bigan hir noise al newe;
For sorwe fayled hir hide and hewe.+
Unto his soule was she ful hold.+
Upon a sauter+ al of gold
To seye the salmes+ faste she bigan,
890 And took no tente+ unto no man.
Than hadde Sir Ywayn muchel drede
For he hoped noght to spede;+
He seyde, "I am muchel to blame
That I love hem that wolde me shame;+
895 But yet I wyte hire al wyth wogh,+
Sith that I hir lord slough.
I can noght see, by no-kyn gynne,+
How that I hir love sholde wynne.
That lady is ful gent and smal,
900 Hir eyen clere as is cristal;
Certes, there is no man alyve

879 **enterement** interment.
883 **chamberere** lady-in-waiting.
886 **fayled hir hide and hewe** i.e., her complexion failed (in color).
887 **hold** loyal.
888 **sauter** psalter.
889 **salmes** psalms.
890 **tente** notice.
892 **For he hoped noght to spede** i.e., because he did not expect to have any success.
894 **shame** harm.
895 **wyte . . . wyth wogh** blame wrongly.
897 **gynne** device, contrivance.

That couthe hir beautesse wel descrive."
Thus was Sir Ywayn stad that sesoun;
He wroghte ful muchel ayeins resoun
905 To sette his love in swich a stede
Wher they hatede him to the dede.+
He seyde he sholde have hire to wyf,
Or elles he sholde lese his lyf.
    Thus as he in studie+ sat,
910 The mayden cam to him wyth that.
She seyde, "How hastow faren this day,
Sith that I went from thee awey?"
Soon she saw him pale and wan,
She wiste wel what ayled than;
915 She seyde, "I wot thyn herte is set;
And certes I shal noght it lette,+
But I shal helpe thee from prisoun
And brynge thee to thy warisoun."+
He seyde, "Certes, Damysele,
920 Out of this place wyl I noght stele.
But I wyl wende by dayes light,
That men mowe of me have sight
Openly on ilke side;
Worthe of me what so bitide,+
925 Manly wyl I hennes wende."
Than answerde the mayden hende,
"Sire, thou shalt wende wyth honour,
For thou shalt have ful good socour.
But, Sire, thou shalt be heer certeyn
930 A while, until I come ageyn."
    She kende al trewely his entente,

906 **dede** = *deeth.*
909 **studie** desire, meditation.
916 **lette** hinder.
918 **warisoun** reward.
924 **Worthe of me what so bitide** i.e., come what may.

173

And ther-fore is she wightly⁺ went
Unto the lady, faire and brighte;
For unto hire right wel she myghte
935 Seye what som hir wylles⁺ is:
For she was al hir maistrise,
Hir keper and hir counseiler.
To hire she seyde as ye shulle here,
Bitwixe hem two in good counseil.
940 "Madame," she seyde, "I have merveil
That ye sorwe thus evere anon.
For Goddes love, lat be your mone:
Ye sholde thenke, over al-kyn thyng,
Of the Kynges Arthur comyng.
945 Meneth you noght⁺ of the message
Of the Damysel Savage,
That in hir lettre to you sende?
Allas, who shal you now defende,
Youre lond, and al that is ther-inne,
950 Sith ye wol nevere of wepyng blynne?
A! Madame, taketh tente⁺ to me!
Ye ne have no knight in this contree
That durste right now his body bede⁺
For-to do a doughty dede,
955 Ne for-to bide⁺ a muchel boste⁺
Of Kyng Arthur and of his ost;⁺
And if he fynde non him ageyn,
Youre londes ben lorn, this is certeyn."
The lady understood ful wel

932 **wightly** quickly.
935 **wylles** wishes.
945 **Meneth you noght** don't you reall.
951 **tente** heed.
953 **bede** offer, commit.
955 **bide** withstand. **boste** menace, threat.
956 **ost** host, army.

960 How she hire counseiled ilke deel.⁺
    She bad hire gon hir weye smertly,
    And that she were no more hardy
    Swiche wordes to hire to speke.
    For wo hir herte wolde al to-breke.
965 She bad, "Go wightly hennes aweye."
    Than the mayden thus gan seye,
    "Madame, it is ofte wommens wylle
    Hem for-to blame that seyth hem skile."⁺
    She wente awey as she noght roghte;⁺
970 And than the lady hire bithoghte
    That the mayden seyde no wrong;
    And so she sat in studie longe.
       In studie thus allone she sat;
    The mayden cam ageyn wyth that.
975 "Madame," she seyde, "ye ben a barn!⁺
    Thus mowe ye soon youre self forfarn;"⁺
    She seyde, "Chastise thyn herte, Madame:
    To swich a lady it is greet shame
    Thus to wepe and make swich cry.
980 Thenke upon thy greet gentry:
    Trowest thou the flour of chivalry
    Sholde al wyth thy lord dy,⁺
    And wyth him be put in molde?⁺
    God forbede that it so sholde!
985 As good as he and bettre ben."
    "Thou liest," she seyde, "by Hevene-Quene!
    Lat see, if thou me telle can

960 **ilke deel** every bit, altogether.
968 **skile** reason.
969 **roghte** cared.
975 **barn** child.
976 **forfarn** ruin, destroy.
982 **dy** = *deye* die.
983 **molde** the earth.

Wher is any so doughty man
As he was that wedded me."
990 "Yis, and ye conne me no maugree,+
And that ye make me sikernesse+
That ye shulle love me nevere the lesse."
She seyde, "Thou mayst be ful certeyn
That for no-thyng that thou mayst seyn
995 Wyl I me wrethe+ on non manere."
"Madame," she seyde, "than shulle ye here.
I shal you telle a privetee,
And no more shal it wite but we.
If two knightes be in the felde
1000 On two stedes, wyth spere and shelde,
And that oon that other may slo,+
Whether+ is the bettre of tho?"
She seyde, "He that has the bataile."
"Yee," seyde the mayden, "sans faile,
1005 The knight that lyveth is more of mayn
Thanne youre lord that was slayn.
Youre lord fledde out of the place,
And that other gan him chace
Hider into his owene hold:
1010 Ther mowe ye wite he was ful bold."
The lady seyde, "This is greet scorn
That thou neveneth+ him me biforn!
Thou seyst nother sooth ne right!
Swith out of myn eyen sight!"
1015 The mayden seyde, "So moot I thee,
Thus ne highte+ ye noght me,

990 **maugree** ill will.
991 **sikernesse** surety, assurance.
995 **wrethe** become angry.
1001 **slo** = *slee.*
1002 **Whether** which (of the two).
1012 **neveneth** mention, name.
1016 **highte** promised.

That ye sholde so me mys-seye."+
Wyth that she turned hire aweye
And hastily she went ageyn
1020 Unto the chambre to Sir Ywayn.
The lady thoghte than al the nyght
How that she hadde no knight,
For-to seche hir lond thurgh-oute
To kepe Arthur and his route.
1025 Than bigan hire for-to shame,
And hirself faste for-to blame;
Unto hirself faste gan she flyte,+
And seyde, "Wyth wronge now I hire wyte:+
Now hopeth she I wyl nevere mare+
1030 Love hire as I have don are.+
I wyl hire love wyth mayn and mood,
For that she seyde was for my good!"
      On the morne the mayden ros
And unto the chambre soon she gos.+
1035 Ther she fyndeth the faire lady
Hongynge hir heed ful drerily,
In the place wher she hire lefte;
And ilke deel she tolde hire efte
As she hadde seyd to hire bifore.
1040 Than seyde the lady, "Me reweth sore
That I mys-seyde thee yesterday:
I wyl amende, if that I may.
Of that knight now wolde I here—
What he were, and whennes he were.
1045 I wot that I have seyd amys:

1017 **mys-seye** abuse.
1027 **flyte** (to) argue, contend.
1028 **wyte** blame.
1029 **mare** = *more.*
1030 **are** = *er.*
1034 **gos** = *goth.*

Now wyl I don as thou me wisse.+
Tel me boldely, er thou blynne,
If he be comen of gentil kynne."
"Madame," she seyde, "I dar warande+
1050 A gentler lord is non lyvande;+
The hendest man ye shulle him fynde
That evere cam of Adames kynde."
"How hot he?+ Sey me for certeyn."
"Madame," she seyde, "Sir Ywayn.
1055 So gentil a knight have ye noght seen:
He is the kynges sone Urien."
She heeld hire payed+ of that tidyng,
For that his fader was a kyng;
"Do me have him heer in my sight
1060 Bitwene this and the thridde nyght—
And erre, if that it erre myghte be:
Me longeth sore him for-to see.
Bryng him, if thou mayst, this nyght!"
"Madame," she seyde, "that I ne myghte,
1065 For his wonyng+ is hennes awey
More thanne the journee of a day.
But I have a wel-rennyng page
Wyl sterte thider right in a stage,+
And brynge him by to-morne at nyghte."
1070 The lady seyde, "Loke if he myghte
To-morne by even be heer ageyn."
She seyde, "Madame, wyth al his mayn."
"Bid him hye on al-kyn wyse;

1046 **wisse** direct.
1049 **warande** warrant.
1050 **lyvande** = *lyvynge.*
1053 **How hot he** what is he called.
1057 **payed** satisfied, pleased.
1065 **wonyng** dwelling.
1068 **right in a stage** i.e., quickly.

He shal be quit wel his servise:
1075 Avauncement shal be his boon+
If he wyl do this erand soon."
"Madame," she seyde, "I dar you highte+
To have him heer er the thridde nyght.
To-whiles,+ after youre counseil sende
1080 And axe hem who shal you defende—
Youre welle, youre lond, castel and tour
Ayeins the noble Kyng Arthur;
For ther is non of hem ilkane+
That dar the bataile undertane.+
1085 Than shulle ye seye, 'Nedes bus me+ take
A lord, to do that ye forsake.'
Nedes bus you have som noble knight
That wyl and may defende youre right.
And seye also, to suffre dede+
1090 Ye wol noght do out of+ her rede.
Of that word shulle they be blithe
And thonke you ful many sithe."
The lady seyde, "By God of myght,
I shal aresone+ hem this nyght.
1095 Me thinketh thou dwellest ful longe heer:
Send forth swithe thy messager!"
Than was the lady blithe and glad:
She dide al as hir mayden bad.
After hir counseil she sente anon,
1100 And bad they sholde come soon echoon.

1075 **boon** reward.
1077 **highte** promise.
1079 **To-whiles** meantime.
1083 **ilkane** each one, all.
1084 **undertane** undertake.
1085 **Nedes bus me** (it) behooves me (to).
1089 **dede** = *deeth*.
1090 **do out of** i.e., act apart from.
1094 **aresone** summon (to council).

The mayden redies hire ful rathe;+
Blive+ she gert+ Sir Ywayn bathe,
And cladde him sithen in good scarlet,
Furred wel, and wyth gold fret;
1105 A girdel ful riche for the nones,
Of perrye+ and of precious stones.
She tolde him al how he sholde do
Whan that he come the lady to.
And thus, whan he was al redy,
1110 She went and tolde to hir lady
That comen was hir messager.
She seyde smertly, "Do lat me here:
Cometh he soon, as have thou wynne?"+
"Madame," she seyde, "I shal noght blynne
1115 Er-that he be bifore you heer."
Than seyde the lady, wyth light chere,
Go bryng him hider prively,
That non wite but thou and I."
Than the mayden went ageyn
1120 Hastily to Sir Ywayn;
"Sire," she seyde, "as have I wynne,
My lady wot thou art heer-inne.
To come bifore hire loke thou be bold,
And tak good tente+ what I have tolde."
1125   By the hond she took the knight,
And ledde him into the chambre right
Bifore hir lady (is noght at layn+);
And of that coom she was ful fayn.
But yet Sir Ywayn hadde greet drede

1101 **rathe** quickly.
1102 **Blive** at once. **gert** prepared.
1106 **perrye** jewels.
1113 **as have thou wynne** as you have honor.
1124 **tente** heed.
1127 **at layn** to be hidden.

1130 Whan he unto the chambre yede.
The chambre floor and also the bed
Wyth clothes of gold was al over-spred.
Hire thoghte he was wythouten lak,+
But no word to him she spak;
1135 And he, for drede awey he drough!
Than the mayden stood and lough;+
She seyde, "Maugree+ have this knight
That hast of swich a lady sight
And can noght shewe to hire his nede.
1140 Com forth, Sire; thee thar+ noght drede
That my lady wyl thee smyte:
She loveth thee wel, wythoute lite.+
Prey to hire of hir mercy,
And for thy sake right so shal I,
1145 That she foryeve thee in this stede
Of Salados the Rouse dede,+
That was hir lord, that thou hast slayn."
On knees him sette than Sir Ywayn:
"Madame, I yelde me you until,+
1150 Evere to be at youre wyl;
If that I myghte, I ne wolde noght flee."
She seyde, "Nay, why sholde so be?
To deeth if I gert do thee now,
To me it were ful litel prow.+
1155 But for I fynde thee so buxome,+
That thou wolde thus to me come,

1133 **lak** lack, defect.
1136 **lough** laughed.
1137 **Maugree** ill luck.
1140 **thar** need.
1142 **wythoute lite** without flaw, fail.
1146 **dede** = *deeth.*
1149 **until** unto.
1154 **prow** benefit.
1155 **buxome** willing, obedient.

And for thou dost thee in my grace,
I foryeve thee thy trespas.
"Sit doun," she seyde, "and lat me here
1160   Why thou are thus debonaire."+
"Madame," he seyde, "ones wyth a look
Al myn herte wyth thee thou took;
Sith I first of thee hadde sight,
Have I thee loved wyth al my myght.
1165   To more thanne thee, my lady hende,
Shal nevere more my love wende.
For thy love evere I am redy
Lely+ for-to lyve or dy."+
She seyde, "Darst thou wel undertake
1170   In my lond pees for-to make,
And for-to mayntene alle my rightes
Ayeins Kyng Arthur and his knightes?"
He seyde, "That dar I undertane+
Ayeines ilke lyvynge man."
1175   Swich counseil bifore hadde she tane;+
She seyde, "Sire, than ben we at ane."+
    Hir barouns hire ful rathly redde+
To take a lord hire for-to wedde.
Than hastily she went to halle.
1180   Ther abide hir barouns alle
For-to holde her parlement
And marye hire by her assent.
She seyde, "Sires, wyth oon acord,
Sith me bus nedely+ have a lord

1160 **debonaire** meek.
1168 **Lely** loyally. **dy** = *deye*.
1173 **undertane** undertake.
1175 **tane** = *taken*.
1176 **at ane** = *at oon* at one, in agreement.
1177 **redde** = *radde* advised.
1184 **me bus nedely** (it) behooves me (to).

1185 My londes for-to lede and yeme,+
   Seyth me soon how ye wol deme."
   "Madame," they seyde, "how so ye wylle,
   Alle we shulle assente ther-tille."+
   Than the lady went ageyn
1190 Unto the chambre of Sir Ywayn.
   "Sire," she seyde, "so God me save,
   Other lord wyl I non have;
   If I thee lefte, I dide noght right,
   A kyng sone and a noble knight."
1195 Now hath the mayden don hir thoght—
   Sir Ywayn out of anger+ broght.
   The lady ledde him unto halle;
   Ayeins him rise the barouns alle,
   And alle they seyde, ful sikerly,
1200 "This knight shal wedde the lady."
   And echoon seyde, hemselve bitwene,
   So faire a man hadde they noght sene:
   "For his beautee in halle and bour,
   Him semeth to ben an emperour.
1205 We wolde that he were trouth-plight
   And wedded soon this ilke nyght."
   The lady sette hire on the dees+
   And comaunded alle to holde her pees,
   And bad hir styward somwhat seye
1210 Er men went from court aweye.
   The styward seyde, "Sires, understandes,+
   Werre+ is waxen in thise londes:
   The Kyng Arthur is redy dight

1185 **lede and yeme** govern and protect.
1188 **ther-tille** thereto.
1196 **anger** trouble, affliction.
1207 **dees** dais, throne.
1211 **understandes** = *understondeth*.
1212 **Werre** war.

To ben heer binne⁺ this fourtenyght;

1215 He and his meynee have thoght
To wynne this lond, if they moghte;⁺
They wite ful wel that he is deed
That was lord heer in this stede.
Non is so wight wepens to welde,

1220 Ne that so boldely may us belde;⁺
And wommen may mayntene no stour,
They mote nedes have a governour.
Ther-fore my lady moot nede
Be wedded hastily for drede;

1225 And to no lord wyl she take tente
But if it be by youre assente."
Than the lordes al on rawe⁺
Helde hem wel payed of this sawe;⁺
Alle assented hire until

1230 To take a lord at hir owene wyl.
Than seyde the lady anon-right,
"How holde ye you payed of this knight?
He profreth him on alle wyse
To myn honour and my servise;

1235 And certes, Sires, the sooth to seye,
I saw him nevere er this day;
But tolde unto me hath it ben
He is the kyng sone Urien;
He is comen of heighe parage

1240 And wonder doughty of vassalage,⁺
War and wys, and ful curteis.

1214 **binne** within.
1216 **moghte** = *myghte*.
1219–20 **Non is so wight wepens to welde, / Ne that so boldely may us belde** i.e., none is courageous enough to wield weapons, nor (is there anyone) that so valiantly may embolden us.
1227 **rawe** = *rowe*, i.e., in turn.
1228 **sawe** speech.
1240 **vassalage** prowess.

He yerneth me to wyfe alweys,
And nevere the lasse, I wot he myghte
Have wel bettre, and so were right."
1245 Wyth oon vois hoolly they seyde,
"Madame, ful wel we holde us payde.
But hasteth faste, al that ye may,+
That ye were wedded this ilke day;"
And greet preyere gonne they make
1250 On alle wyse that she sholde him take.
Soon unto the chirche they wente
And were wedded in her presente:+
Ther wedded Ywayn in plevyne+
The riche Lady Alundyne,
1255 The dukes doghter of Landuit—
Elles hadde hir lond ben destruit.+
Thus they made the mariage
Among al the riche baronage;
They made ful muchel myrthe that day,
1260 Ful grete festes on good array.
Grete myrthes made they in that stede,
And al foryeten is now the dede+
Of him that was her lord free;
They seye that this+ is worth swiche three,
1265 And that they lovede him muchel more
Thanne him that was her lord bifore.

The bridal sat, for sooth to telle,
Til Kyng Arthur cam to the welle
Wyth alle his knightes everichoon;

1247 **may** = *mowe* may.
1252 **presente** presence.
1253 **plevyne** pledge.
1256 **destruit** destroyed.
1262 **dede** = *deeth.*
1264 **this** i.e., this (new) lord.

1270　Bihynde leved+ ther noght oon.
　　　Than seyde Sir Kay, "Now wher is he
　　　That made swich boste heer for-to be,
　　　For-to venge his cosin-germain?
　　　I wiste his wordes were alle in vayne:
1275　He made greet boste bifore the quene,
　　　And heer now dar he noght be sene!
　　　His proude wordes ben now al purst,+
　　　For in feith ful ille he durste
　　　Ones loke upon that knight
1280　That he made boste wyth to fighte."
　　　Than seyde Gawayn hastily,
　　　"Sire, for Goddes love, mercy!
　　　For I dar hete+ thee for certeyn
　　　That we shulle here of Sir Ywayn
1285　This ilke day, that be thou bold,+
　　　But he be deed or don in hold;
　　　And nevere in no companye
　　　Herde I him speke thee vilanye."
　　　Than seyde Sir Kay, "Lo, at thy wylle
1290　From this tyme forth I shal be stille."
　　　　　The kyng caste water upon the ston;
　　　The storm ros ful soon anon
　　　Wyth wikked weders kene and cold,
　　　As it was bifore-hond told.
1295　The kyng and his men ilkane+
　　　Wende ther-wyth to have ben slane,+
　　　So blewe it stour,+ wyth sleet and reyn!
　　　And hastily than Sir Ywayn

1270 **leved** stopped, remained.
1277 **purst** withdrawn.
1283 **hete** promise.
1285 **that be . . . bold** i.e., be certain of it.
1295 **ilkane** = *echoon.*
1296 **slane** = *slayn.*
1297 **stour** violently.

Dighte him graythly⁺ in his gere,

1300 Wyth noble shelde and strong spere.
Whan he was dight in siker wede,
Than he umstrod⁺ a noble stede;
Him thoghte that he was as light
As a fowel is to the flyght.

1305 Unto the welle faste wendeth he,
And soon, whan they him myghte see,
Sir Kay—for he wolde fyghte noght fayle—
Smertly axeth the bataile;
And as soon than seyde the kyng,

1310 "Sire Kay, I graunte thee thyn axyng."
Than Sir Ywayn neighed hem nere
Her countenaunce⁺ to see and here;
Sir Kay than on his stede gan sprynge.
"Ber thee wel now," seyde the kyng.

1315 Ful glad and blithe was Sir Ywayn
Whan Sir Kay cam him ageyn;
But Kay wiste noght who it was:
He fyndeth his fere⁺ now er he passe!⁺
Sir Ywayn thenketh now to be wroken⁺

1320 On the grete wordes that Kay hadde spoken.
They ride togidre wyth speres kene–
Ther was no reverence⁺ hem bitwene.
Sir Ywayn gan Sir Kay bere
Out of his sadel lengthe of his spere;

1325 His helm unto the erthe smot:
A fote⁺ depe ther-inne it bot.⁺

1299 **Dighte him graythly** arrayed himself properly.
1302 **umstrod** mounted.
1312 **countenaunce** demeanor.
1318 **fere** match. **passe** goes (forth).
1319 **wroken** avenged.
1322 **reverence** respect, forbearance.
1326 **fote** = *foot*. **bot** bit.

He wolde don him no more despite,
But doun he lighted as tite;
Sir Kay stede he took in hye
1330 And presente the kyng ful curteisly.
Wonder glade than were they alle
That Kay so foul a shame gan falle.
And echoon seyde to other then,+
"This is he that scorneth alle men;"
1335 Of his wo were they wel payde.
Sir Ywayn than to the kyng seyde,
"Sire Kyng, I yeve to thee this stede,
For he may helpe thee in thy nede;
And to me were it greet trespas
1340 For-to wyth-holde that youres was."
"What man artow?" quod the kyng;
"Of thee have I no knowyng,
But if thou unarmed were,
Or elles thy name that I myghte here."
1345 "Lord," he seyde, "I am Ywayn."
    Than was the kyng ferly+ fayn;
A sory man than was Sir Kay,
That seyde that he was stolen awey!
Al disconfit+ he lay on grounde:
1350 To him that was a sory stounde.
The kyng and his men were ful glade
That they so Sir Ywayn hadde;
And ful glad was Sir Gawayn
Of the welfare of Sir Ywayn:
1355 For non was to him half so dere
Of alle that in the court were.
The kyng Sir Ywayn soon bisoghte
To telle him al how he hadde wrought;

1333 **then** = *than*.
1346 **ferly** wondrously.
1349 **disconfit** discomfited.

And soon Sir Ywayn gan him telle
1360 Of al his fare, how it bifel:
Wyth the knight how that he spedde,
And how he hadde the lady wedd,
And how the mayden him helped wel—
Thus tolde he to him ilke deel.
1365 "Sire Kyng," he seyde, "I you biseche,
And al youre meynee, mylde and meke,
That ye wolde graunte to me that grace
To wende wyth me to my purchace, +
And see my castel and my tour:
1370 Than myghte ye do me greet honour."
The kyng graunted him ful right
To dwelle wyth him a fourtenyght.
Sir Ywayn thonked him ofte sithe; +
The knightes were alle glade and blithe
1375 Wyth Sir Ywayn for-to wende.
And soon a squier hath he send: +
Unto the castel the weye he nom +
And warned the lady of her coom,
And that his lord cam wyth the kyng.
1380 And whan the lady herde this thyng,
It is no lyvynge man wyth mouthe
That half hir confort + telle couthe.
Hastily that lady hende
Comaunded alle hir men to wende
1385 And dighten hem in her beste array,
To kepe + the kyng that ilke day.
They kepede him in riche wede,

1368 **purchace** gains, possessions.
1373 **ofte sithe** many times.
1376 **send** = *sent.*
1377 **nom** took.
1382 **confort** pleasure.
1386 **kepe** receive.

Ridynge on many a noble stede;
They halsede+ him ful curteisly,
1390 And also al his companye;
They seyde he was a worthy to doute+
That so fele+ folk ledde aboute.
Ther was greet joye, I you bihete,
Wyth clothes spradde on ilke strete;
1395 And damyselles dauncynge ful wel
Wyth trompes,+ pipes, and wyth fristele.+
The castel and the citee ronge
Wyth mynstralcye and noble song.
They ordeynde hem, echoon in fere,
1400 To kepe the kyng on faire manere.
The lady went wythouten toun,
And wyth hire many bolde baroun,
Clad in purpre and ermine,
Wyth girdels al of gold ful fyne.
1405 The lady made ful myrie chere:
She was all dight wyth drueries+ dere.
Aboute hire was ful muchel throng:
The peple cried and seyde among,
"Welcome artow, Kyng Arthur!
1410 Of al this world thou berest the flour:
Lord kyng of alle kynges,
And blessed be He that thee brynges!"+
    Whan the lady the kyng saw,
Unto him faste gan she drawe
1415 To holde his styrop whil he light.
But soon whan he of hire hadde sight,

1389 **halsede** greeted.
1391 **doute** fear.
1392 **fele** many.
1396 **trompes** trumpets. **fristele** flutes.
1406 **drueries** gifts.
1412 **brynges** = *bryngeth.*

Wyth muchel myrthe they samen⁺ mette.
Wyth hende wordes she him grette,
"A thousand sithes welcome," she seys,⁺
1420 "And so is Sir Gawayn the curteis."
The kyng seyde, "Lady, white so the flour,
God yeve thee joye and muchel honour,
For thou art faire wyth body gent."
Wyth that he hire in armes hente,
1425 And ful faire he gan hire folde:⁺
Ther was many to biholde.
It is no man wyth tonge may telle
The myrthe that was hem a-melle.⁺
Of maydens was ther so good won⁺
1430 That ilke knight myghte take oon.
Ful muchel joye Sir Ywayn made
That he the kyng to his hous hadde;
The lady among hem al samen
Made ful muchel joye and gamen.
1435 In the castel thus they dwelle:
Ful muchel myrthe was hem a-melle.
The kyng was ther wyth his knightes
Eighte dayes and eighte nyghtes,
And Ywayn hem ful myrie made
1440 Wyth al-kyn gamen hem for-to gladde.
He preyde the kyng to thonke the may
That him hadde helped in his journee;
And ech day hadde they solas sere⁺
Of huntyng and also of ryvere;⁺

1417 **samen** together.
1419 **seys** = *seyth.*
1425 **folde** enfold, embrace.
1428 **a-melle** among.
1429 **so good won** a very good number.
1443 **solas sere** various enjoyments.
1444 **ryvere** i.e., of hawking.

1445 For ther was a ful faire contree,
Wyth wodes and parkes greet plentee,
And castels wroght wyth lyme and stane,+
That Ywayn wyth his wyf hadde tane.

Now wyl the kyng no lenger lende,+
1450 But to his contree wyl he wende.
A-whiles+ they were ther, for certeyn,
Sir Gawayn dide al his mayn
To preye Sir Ywayn on al manere
For-to wende wyth him y-fere.+
1455 He seyde, "Sire, if thou lie at hame,+
Wonderly men wol thee blame.
That knight is no-thyng to sette by
That leveth al his chivalry
And lieth bekynge+ in his bed,
1460 Whan he hath a lady wedd.
For whan that he hath greet endos,+
Than were tyme to wynne his los;+
For whan a knight is chivalrous
His lady is the more jelous,
1465 Also she loveth him wel the bette.+
Ther-fore, Sire, thou shalt noght lette
To haunte+ armes in ech contree;
Than wol men wel more preyse thee.
Thou hast ynough at thy despense;

1447 **stane** = *ston(e)*.
1449 **lende** remain.
1451 **A-whiles** all the time (that).
1454 **y-fere** together, in company.
1455 **hame** = *hom(e)*.
1459 **bekynge** warming (himself).
1461 **endos** (?) things to be done.
1462 **los** fame.
1465 **bette** better.
1467 **haunte** practice, follow.

1470 Now may thou wel haunte tourneymentes.
Thou and I shulle wende y-fere,
And I wyl be at thy banere.
I dar noght seye, so God me gladde,
If I so faire a lemman hadde,
1475 That I ne moot leve al chivalry
At home idel wyth hire to lie.
But yet a fool that litel can
May wel counseile an other man."
So longe Sir Gawayn preyde so,
1480 Sir Ywayn graunteth him for-to go
Unto the lady and take his leve;
Loth him was hire for-to greve.
To hire anon the weye he nam,
But she ne wiste noght why he cam.
1485 In his armes he gan hire mete,+
And thus he seyde, "My lemman swete,
My lyf, myn hele, and al myn herte,
My joye, my confort, and my querte,+
A thyng preye I thee unto
1490 For thyn honour and myn also."
The lady seyde, "Sire, verrayment,+
I wyl do al youre comaundement."
"Dame," he seyde, "I wyl thee preye
That I myghte the kyng conveye+
1495 And also wyth my feres+ founde
Armes for-to haunte a stounde.
For in bourdyng+ men wolde me blame,
If I sholde now dwelle at hame."+

1485 **mete** embrace.
1488 **querte** health.
1491 **verrayment** truly.
1494 **conveye** accompany.
1495 **feres** companions.
1497 **bourdyng** jestings.
1498 **hame** = hom(e).

The lady was loth him to greve;
1500   "Sire," she seyde, "I yeve you leve
Until a terme that I shal seyn,
But that ye come than ageyn!
Al this yeer hol I you graunte
Dedes of armes for-to haunte;
1505   But, Sire, as ye love me dere,
On alle wyse that ye ben here+
This twelve-month how som it be,
For the love ye owe to me.
And if ye come noght by that day,
1510   My love shulle ye lese for ay.
Avise you wel now er ye gon.
This day is the even of Seint John;
That warne I you now er ye wende,
Loke ye come by the twelve-month ende."
1515   "Dame," he seyde, "I shal noght lete
To holde the day that thou hast set;
And if I myght be at my wyl,
Ful ofte erre sholde I come thee til.+
But, Madame, this understondes,+
1520   A man that passeth diverse londes
May som-tyme come in greet distresse,
In prisoun or elles in siknesse;
Ther-fore I preye you, er I go,
That ye wol out-take+ thise two."
1525   The lady seyde, "This graunte I wel,
As ye axe, everich a deel;
And I shal lene+ to you my ryng,
That is to me a ful dere thyng:

1506 **here** = *heer.*
1518 **til** to.
1519 **understondes** = *understondeth.*
1524 **out-take** exclude.
1527 **lene** give.

In non anger+ shulle ye be
1530 Whil ye it have and thenke on me.
I shal telle to you anon
The vertue+ that is in the ston:
It is no prisoun you shal holde,
Al if youre fos+ be many-folde.
1535 Wyth siknesse shulle ye noght be tane,
Ne of youre blood ye shulle lese nane;+
In bataile taken shulle ye noght be
Whil ye it have and thenke on me;
And ay, whil ye ben trewe of love,
1540 Over al shulle ye ben above.
I wolde nevere for no-kyn wight
Lene it er unto no knight;
For greet love I it you take:+
Yemeth+ it wel now for my sake."
1545   Sir Ywayn seyde, "Dame, gramercy!"
Than he gert ordeyne+ in hye
Armures and al other gere,
Stalworth stedes, bothe sheeld and spere,
And also squier, knave, and swayn.
1550 Ful glad and blithe was Sir Gawayn.
No lenger wolde Sir Ywayn bide;
On his stede soon gan he stride:
And thus he hath his leve tane—
For him murnde many ane.+
1555 The lady took leve of the kyng

1529 **anger** affliction.
1532 **vertue** power.
1534 **fos** foes.
1536 **nane** = *non.*
1543 **take** give.
1544 **Yemeth** take care (of).
1546 **gert ordeyne** caused to make ready.
1554 **ane** = *oon.*

And of his meynee, olde and yinge; +
Hir lord, Sir Ywayn, she biseches,
Wyth teres triklynge on hir chekes,
On alle wyse that he noght lete
1560   To holde the day that he hadde set.
     The knightes thus her weyes ben went
To justyng and to tourneyment.
Ful doughtily dide Sir Ywayn,
And also dide Sir Gawayn;
1565   They were ful doughty bothe y-fere—
They wonne the pris bothe fer and nere.
The kyng that tyme at Chester lay.
The knightes wente hem forth to pleye:
Ful redily they ride aboute
1570   Al that twelve-month oute and oute
To justyng and to tourneyment.
They wonne grete worshipes as they went.
Sir Ywayn ofte hadde al the los: +
Of him the word ful wide gos. +
1575   Of her dedes was greet renoun
To and fro in tour and toun.
On this wyse in this lyf they laste
Until Seint Johnnes day was past;
Than hastily they hyede home
1580   And soon unto the kyng they come;
And ther they helde greet mangery, +
The kyng wyth al his companye.
     Sir Ywayn um-bithoghte + him than
He hadde foryeten his lemman:
1585   "Broken I have hir comaundement.

1556 **yinge** = *yonge.*
1573 **los** fame, renoun.
1574 **gos** = *goth.*
1581 **mangery** feast.
1583 **um-bithoghte** recalled, considered.

Certes," he seyde, "now be I shent; +
The terme is past that she me sette.
How evere shal this bale+ be bett?"+
Unethes he myghte him holde from wepe;
1590 And right in this than took he kepe,+
Into court cam a damysel
On a palfrey amblynge wel;
And egrely doun gan she lighte
Wythouten help of knave or knight;
1595 And soon she lete hir mantel falle
And hasted hire faste into halle.
"Sire Kyng," she seyde, "God moot thee see,+
My lady greteth thee wel by me,
And also Sir good Gawayn,
1600 And alle thy knightes but Sir Ywayn.
He is ateyned+ for traitour,
A fals and lither losenjour;+
He hath bitrayed my lady,
But she is war wyth his gilrye.+
1605 She hoped noght, the sooth to seye,
That he wolde so have stole aweye;
He made to hire ful muchel boste,
And seyde of alle he loved hire moste.
Al was tresoun and trecherie,
1610 And that he shal ful dere a-bye.+
It is ful muchel ayeins the right
To calle so fals a man a knight.
My lady wende he hadde hir herte

1586 **shent** ruined.
1588 **bale** affliction. **bett** remedied.
1590 **took . . . kepe** took heed.
1597 **God moot thee see** may God favor you.
1601 **ateyned** condemned.
1602 **lither losenjour** wicked liar.
1604 **gilrye** deception.
1610 **a-bye** pay for.

Ay for-to kepe and holde in querte;+
1615 But now wyth greef he hath hir gret,+
And broken the terme that she him sette,
That was the even of Seint John;
Now is that tyme for evere gon.
So longe yaf she him respite,
1620 And thus he hath hire led wyth lite.+
Certeynly, so fals a fode+
Was nevere come of kynges blood,
That so soon foryat his wyf
That loved him bettre thanne hir lyf."

1625   To Ywayn seyth she thus, "Thou es+
Traitour untrewe and troutheles,
And also an unkynde comlyng.+
Deliver me my lady ryng!"
She stert to him wyth sterne look:
1630 The ryng from his fynger she took.
And as soon as she hadde the ryng,
Hir leve took she of the kyng
And stirte up on hir palfrey.
Wythouten more she wente hir weye.
1635 Wyth hire was nother knave ne grome;
Ne no man wiste wher she bicome.+

   Sir Ywayn, whan he this gan here,
Murnde and made simple chere.+
In sorwe than so was he stad,+

1614 **querte** health.
1615 **gret** greeted.
1620 **led wyth lite** i.e., treated viciously.
1621 **fode** creature.
1625 **es** = *art*.
1627 **comlyng** newcomer, upstart.
1636 **bicome** = *bicam*.
1638 **chere** appearance, disposition.
1639 **stad** placed, situated.

1640 That nere for murnyng wex he madd.
　　　It was no myrthe that him myghte mende—
　　　To worthe⁺ to noght ful wel he wende,
　　　For wo he is ful wyl of wane.⁺
　　　"Allas, I am myn owene bane.⁺
1645 Allas," he seyde, "that I was born,
　　　Have I my lemman thus forlorn:
　　　And al is for myn owene folye.
　　　Allas, this dol wyl make me deye."
　　　An yvel took him as he stood;
1650 For wo he wex al wilde and wood.
　　　Unto the wode the weye he nam—
　　　No man wiste wher he bicam.
　　　Aboute he walked in the foreste,
　　　As it were a wilde beste;
1655 His men on ilke side have soght
　　　Fer and nere and fynden him noght.
　　　　On a day as Ywayn ran
　　　In the wode, he mette a man;
　　　Arwes brode and bowe hadde he,
1660 And whan Sir Ywayn gan him see,
　　　To him he stirte wyth bir⁺ ful grym,
　　　His bowe and arwes refte⁺ he him.
　　　Ilke day than atte leste
　　　Sheet⁺ he him a wilde beste;
1665 Flessh he wan him ful good won,⁺
　　　And of his arwes loste he non.
　　　Ther he lyvde a greet sesoun

1642 **worthe** become, come.
1643 **wyl of wane** i.e., homeless.
1644 **bane** slayer, death.
1661 **bir** assault.
1662 **refte** bereft, robbed.
1664 **Sheet** shot.
1665 **won** abundance.

Wyth rotes and rawe venysoun;
He drank of the warme blood,
1670 And that dide him muchel good.
    As he went in that buskage+
He fond a litel hermitage.
The hermite saw and soon was war
A naked man a bowe bar.
1675 He hoped he was wood+ that tide;
Ther-fore no lenger durste he bide.
He sparred+ his yate and in he ran,
Forfered+ of that wode man;
And for him thoghte it charitee,
1680 Out at his wyndow sette he
Breed and water for the wode man;
And ther-to ful soon he ran.
Swich as he hadde, swich he him yaf—
Barly-breed wyth al the chaf;
1685 Ther-of eet he ful good won,
And er swich eet he nevere non;
Of the water he drank ther-wyth;
Than ran he forth into the frith.+
For if a man be nevere so wood,
1690 He wyl come wher man doth him good;
And certeynly so dide Ywayn.
Everich a day he cam ageyn,
And wyth him broghte he redy boun+
Ilke day newe venysoun;
1695 He leyde it at the hermite yate,
And eet and drank and went his gate.+

1671 **buskage** wooded area.
1675 **hoped he was wood** supposed he was mad.
1677 **sparred** fastened.
1678 **Forfered** quite frightened.
1688 **frith** woodland.
1693 **boun** prepared.
1696 **gate** way, path.

Evere as soon as he was gon
The hermite took the flessh anon;
He flough+ it and seeth+ it faire and wel;
1700 Than hadde Ywayn at ilke mele
Breed and soden+ venysoun.
Than went hermite to the toun
And solde the skinnes that he broghte,
And bettre breed ther-wyth he boghte;
1705 Than fond Sir Ywayn in that stede
Venysoun and bettre breed.
This lyf ledde he ful fele yere,
And sithen he wroghte as ye shulle here.

As Ywayn sleped under tree,
1710 By him come ther ridynge three—
A lady, two boure-wommen+ also.
Than spak oon of the maydens two,
"A naked man me think'th I see;
Wite I wyl what it may be."
1715 She lighted doun and to him yede,
And unto him she took good hede;
Hir thoghte wel she hadde him seen
In many stedes wher she hadde ben.
She was astonyed+ in that stounde,
1720 For in his face she saw a wounde,
But it was heled and hol of hewe;
Ther-by hir thoghte that she him knew.
She seyde, "By God that me hath made,
Swich a wounde Sir Ywayn hadde:
1725 Certeynly this ilk+ is he.

1699 **flough** flayed. **seeth** boiled.
1701 **soden** boiled.
1711 **boure-wommen** ladies-in-waiting.
1719 **astonyed** astonished.
1725 **this ilk** this same (man).

Allas," she seyde, "how may this be?
Allas, that him is thus bitidd,
So noble a knight as he was kidd.+
It is greet sorwe that he sholde be
1730 So ugly now upon to see."
So tendrely for him she grette+
That hir teres al hir chekes wette.
"Madame," she seyde, "for certeyn,
Heer have we founde Sir Ywayn,
1735 The beste knight that on grounde may go.
Allas, him is bitidd so wo.
In som sorwe was he stad,
And ther-fore is he waxen madd.
Sorwe wyl menge+ a mannes blood
1740 And make him for-to waxen wood.
Madame, and he were not in querte+
And al hol of wylle and herte,
Ayeins youre fo he wolde you were,+
That hath you don so muchel dere.+
1745 And he were hol, so God me mende,
Youre sorwe were soon broght to ende."
The lady seyde, "And this ilk be he
And that he wyl noght hennes flee,
Thurgh Goddes help than hope I yet
1750 We shulle him wynne into his wyt.
Swithe at hom I wolde we were,
For ther I have an oynement dere;
Morgan the Wys yaf it to me

1728 **kidd** known (to be).
1731 **grette** wept.
1739 **menge** stir, mix.
1741 **querte** health.
1743 **were** defend, protect.
1744 **dere** harm.
1745 *me* for MS. *we.*

And seyde as I shal telle to thee.
1755 He seyde, 'This oynement is so good,
That if a man be brayne-wood
And he were ones anoynt wyth it,
Smertly sholde he have his wyt.' "
From hom they were but half a myle;
1760 Thider come they in a while.
The lady soon the boyste+ hath soght,
And the oynement hath she broght.
"Have," she seyde, "this oynement here,
Unto me it is ful dere;
1765 And smertly that thou wende ageyn.
But loke thou spende it noght in vayn;
And from the knight anoynted be,
That thou leveth, bryng it to me."
Hastily that mayden meke
1770 Took hose and shoos and serk+ and breke;+
A riche robe als+ gan she ta,+
And a ceynt+ of silk alswa,+
And also a good palfrey;
And smertly cam she wher he lay.
1775 On slepe faste yet she him fond;
Hir hors unto a tree she band
And hastily to him she yede—
And that was a ful hardy dede.
She anoynt his heved+ wel,
1780 And his body ilke deel;
She despended al the oynement
Over hir ladies comaundement.
For hir lady wolde she noght lete;

1761 **boyste** box.
1770 **serk** shirt. **breke** undergarment.
1771 **als** = *also.* **ta** = *take.*
1772 **ceynt** girdle. **alswa** = *also.*
1779 **heved** = *heed* head.

Hir thoghte that it was ful wel set.
1785 Al his atire she lefte him by
At his risyng to be redy,
That he myghte him clothe and dighte
Er he sholde of hire have sight.
    Than he waked of his slepe.
1790 The mayden to him took good kepe.
He loked up ful sorily
And seyde, "Lady Seint Marie,
What harde grace to me is maked+
That I am heer now thus al naked.
1795 Allas, wher any have heer been?
I trowe, som hath my sorwe seen."
Longe he sat so in a thoght
How that gere was thider broght.
Than hadde he noght so muchel myght
1800 On his feet to stonde upright:
Him fayled myght of feet and hond
That he myghte nother go ne stonde.
But yet his clothes on he wan;
Ther-fore ful wery was he than.
1805 Than hadde he mystere+ for-to mete
Som man that myghte his bales bete.+
Than leep the mayden on hir palfrey
And nere biside him made hir weye.
She lete as she hadde noght him seen,
1810 Ne wist that he ther hadde ben.
Soon whan he hadde of hire had sight,
He cried unto hire on hight;
Than wolde she no ferre ride,
But faste she loked on ilke side
1815 And waited aboute fer and nere.

1793 **maked** = *made.*
1805 **mystere** want, need.
1806 **his bales bete** remedy his affliction.

He cried and seyde, "I am here."
Than soon she rod him til
And seyde, "Sire, what is thy wyl?"
"Lady, thy help were me ful leef,
1820 For I am heer in greet myschief:
I ne wot nevere by what chaunce
That I have al this grevaunce.
Par charitee I wolde thee preye
For-to lene me that palfrey
1825 That in thyn honde is redy boun,
And wisse⁺ me soon unto som toun.
I wot noght how I hadde this wo,
Ne how that I shal hennes go."
She answerde him wyth wordes hende,
1830 "Sire, if thou wyl wyth me wende,
Ful gladly wyl I ese thee
Until that thou amended be."
  She helped him up on his hors rigge,⁺
And soon they come unto a brigge;
1835 Into the water the boyste⁺ she caste
And sithen home she hyed faste.
Whan they come to the castel yate,
They lighted and went in ther-at.
The mayden to the chambre went;
1840 The lady axed the oynement.
"Madame," she seyde, "the boyste is lorn,
And so was I nerehonde⁺ ther-forn."
"How so," she seyde, "for Goddes tree?"
"Madame," she seyde, "I shal telle thee
1845 Al the sooth how that it was.
As I over the brigge sholde passe,

1826 **wisse** direct, guide.
1833 **rigge** back.
1835 **boyste** box.
1842 **nerehonde** nearly, almost.

Evene in myddes, the sooth to seye,
Ther stombled my palfrey;
On the brigge he fel al flat,
1850 And the boyste right wyth that
Fel from me in the water doun;
And hadde I noght ben titter boun +
To take my palfrey by the mane,
The water soon hadde ben my bane."
1855 The lady seyde, "Now am I shent,
That I have lorn my good oynement;
It was to me, so God me gladde,
The beste tresour that evere I hadde.
To me it is ful muchel scathe, +
1860 But bettre is lese it thanne you bathe. +
Wend," she seyde, "unto the knight
And loke thou ese him at thy myght."
"Lady," she seyde, "elles were me lathe." +
Than she gert him wasshe and bathe
1865 And yaf him mete and drynk of mayn
Til he hadde geten his myght ageyn.
They ordeynde armures ful wel dight,
And so they dide stedes ful wight.

So it fel soon on a day,
1870 Whil he in the castel lay,
The riche erl, Sir Alers,
Wyth knightes, sergeaunts, + and squiers,
And wyth swithe greet vitaile +
Come that castel to assaile.

1852 **titter boun** more quickly prepared.
1859 **scathe** misfortune, harm.
1860 **bathe** = *bothe.*
1863 **lathe** = *lothe* hateful.
1872 **sergeaunts** servants.
1873 **vitaile** provisions.

1875 Sir Ywayn than his armures tase+
     Wyth other socour that he hase.+
     The erl he kepeth in the felde,
     And soon he hit oon on the shelde
     That the knight and als his stede
1880 Stark deed to the erthe they yede.
     Soon an other, the thridde, the ferthe
     Felde he doun deed on the erthe;
     He stired him so among hem than,
     At ilke dynt he slough+ a man.
1885 Some he lesed of his men,
     But the erl lost swiche ten.
     Alle they fledde faste from that side
     Wher they sawe Sir Ywayn ride.
     He herted so his companye
1890 The moste coward was ful hardy
     To felle alle that they founde in feeld.
         The lady lay evere and biheeld.
     She seyth, "Yon is a noble knight,
     Ful eger and of ful greet myght;
1895 He is wel worthy for-to preyse,
     That is so doughty and curteis."
     The mayden seyde, "Wythouten lette,
     Youre oynement mowe ye thenke wel set:
     See, Madame, how he priketh?+
1900 And see, also, how fele+ he stiketh?
     Lo, how he fareth among his fos;
     Alle that he hitteth soon he slos.+
     Were ther swiche other two as he,

1875 **tase** = *taketh.*
1876 **hase** = *hath.*
1884 **slough** slew.
1899 **priketh** spurs, urges.
1900 **how fele** how many.
1902 **slos** = *sleeth* slays.

Than, hope I, soon her fos sholde flee.
1905 Certes, than sholde we see ful tite
The erl sholde be disconfit.+
Madame, God yeve,+ his wyl were
To wedde you and be lord here."
 The erles folk went faste to dede;+
1910 To flee than was his beste rede.
The erl soon bigan to flee
And than myghte men bourd+ see,
How Sir Ywayn and his feres+
Folwede hem on fele maneres;
1915 And faste they slowe the erles men:
Alyve they lefte noght over ten.
The erl fledde ful faste for drede,
And than Sir Ywayn strok his stede
And overtook him that tide
1920 At a castel ther-biside.
Sir Ywayn soon wyth-sette+ the yate
That the erl myghte noght in ther-at.
The erl saw al myghte noght gayne;
He yolde him soon to Sir Ywayn,
1925 And soon he hath his trouthe plight
To wende wyth him that ilke nyght
Unto the lady of greet renoun
And profre him to hir prisoun,
And to don him in hir grace
1930 And also to mende his trespas.
 The erl than unarmed his heved,+

1906 **disconfit** routed, frustrated.
1907 **God yeve** may God grant.
1909 **dede** = *deeth.*
1912 **bourd** amusement.
1913 **feres** companions.
1921 **wyth-sette** blocked.
1931 **heved** = *heed* head.

And non armure on him he leved.+
Helm, sheeld, and also his brond+
That he bar naked in his hond—
1935   Al he yaf to Sir Ywayn,
And home he went wyth him ageyn.
In the castel made they joye ilkane+
Whan they wiste the erl was tane.
And whan they sawe hem comynge nere,
1940   Ayeins him wente they al y-fere.
And whan the lady gan hem mete,
Sir Ywayn goodly gan hire grete.
He seyde, "Madame, have thy prisoun,
And hold him heer in thy baundoun."+
1945   But he gert hire graunte him grace
To make amendes in that space.
On a book the erl swor
For-to restore bothe lasse and more,
And bige+ ageyn bothe tour and toun
1950   That by him were casten doun,
And evermore to ben hir freend.
Homage made he to that hende;
To this foreward+ he borwes+ fond
The beste lordes of al that lond.
1955   Sir Ywayn wolde no lenger lende,+
But redies him faste for-to wende.
At the lady his leve he taketh;
Greet murnyng ther-fore she maketh.
She seyde, "Sire, if it be youre wylle,

1932 **leved** = *lefte*.
1933 **brond** sword.
1937 **ilkane** = *echoon*.
1944 **baundoun** power.
1949 **bige** (?) build.
1953 **foreward** pledge. **borwes** sureties.
1955 **lende** remain.

1960   I preye you for-to dwelle heer stille:
      And I wyl yelde into youre hondes
      Myn owene body and alle my londes."
      Heer-of faste she him bisoghte,
      But al hir speche avayleth noght.
1965   He seyde, "I wyl no-thyng to mede[+]
      But myn armures and my stede."
      She seyde, "Bothe stede and other thyng
      Ben youres at youre owene likyng;
      And if ye wolde heer-wyth us dwelle,
1970   Muchel myrthe were us a-melle."[+]
      It was no boot to bidde him bide:
      He took his stede and on gan stride.
      The lady and hir maydens gente
      Wepede sore whan that he went.

1975   Now rideth Ywayn as ye shulle here,
      Wyth hevy herte and drery chere
      Thurgh a forest by a sty;[+]
      And ther he herde a hidous cry.
      The gayneste[+] weye ful soon he tas[+]
1980   Til he cam wher the noise was.
      Than was he war of a dragoun
      Hadde assailed a wilde leoun;
      Wyth his tayl he drough him faste,
      And fyr evere on him caste;
1985   The leoun hadde over-litel myght
      Ayeins the dragoun for-to fighte.
      Than Sir Ywayn made him boun
      For-to socoure the leoun.

1965 **to mede** as reward, payment.
1970 **a-melle** among.
1977 **sty** path.
1979 **gayneste** most direct. **tas** = *taketh.*

His sheeld bifore his face he faste⁺

1990 For the fyr that the dragoun caste;
He strok the dragoun in at the chavel⁺
That it cam oute at the navel;
Sonder⁺ strok he the throte-bolle⁺
That from the body went the cholle.⁺

1995 By the leoun tayl the heed heng yet,
For ther-by hadde he take his bit;
The tayl Sir Ywayn strok in two:
The dragoun heed than fel ther-fro.
He thoghte, "If the leoun me assaile,

2000 Redy shal he have bataile."
But the leoun wolde noght fighte:
Greet faunyng made he to the knighte.
Doun on the grounde he sette him ofte,
His forther-feet⁺ he heeld a-lofte,

2005 And thonked the knight as he couthe,
Al if he myghte noght speke wyth mouthe;
So wel the leoun of him lete,⁺
Ful lowe he lay and likked his feet.
Whan Sir Ywayn that sight gan see,

2010 Of the beste him thoghte pitee,
And on his weye forth gan he ride.
The leoun folwed by his side.
In the foreste al that day
The leoun mekely folwed ay,

2015 And nevere for wele ne for wo
Wolde he parte Sir Ywayn fro.

1989 **faste** held in position.
1991 **chavel** jaw.
1993 **Sonder** asunder. **throte-bolle** throatboll, i.e., Adam's apple.
1994 **cholle** flesh under the jaw.
2004 **forther-feet** i.e., forefeet.
2007 **So wel . . . lete** so highly thought.

Thus in the foreste as they wore⁺
The leoun hungred swithe sore.
Of a beste savour⁺ he hadde;
2020 Unto his lord semblaunt he made
That he wolde go to gete his pray;⁺
His kynde⁺ it wolde,⁺ the sooth to seye.
For his lord sholde him noght greve,
He wolde noght go wythouten leve.
2025 From his lord the weye he laught⁺
The mountance⁺ of an arwe-draught;⁺
Soon he mette a bareyn do,⁺
And ful soon he gan hire slo;⁺
Hir throte in two ful soon he bot⁺
2030 And drank the blood whil it was hot.
That do he caste than in his nek
As it were a mele-sak.
Unto his lord than he it bar;
And Sir Ywayn perceived thar⁺
2035 That it was so nere the nyght
That no ferre ride he myghte.
   A logge⁺ of boughes soon he made,
And flynt and fyr-iren bothe he hadde,
And fyr ful soon ther he slough⁺
2040 Of drye mos and many a bough.

2017 **wore** = *were.*
2019 **savour** scent.
2021 **pray** prey.
2022 **kynde** nature. **wolde** willed.
2025 **laught** took.
2026 **mountance** the distance of. **arwe-draught** arrow's flight.
2027 **do** doe.
2028 **slo** = *slee.*
2029 **bot** bit.
2034 **thar** = *ther.*
2037 **logge** lodging.
2039 **slough** struck.

The leoun hath the do undon;
Sir Ywayn made a spit ful soon,
And rosted som to her soupere.
The leoun lay as ye shulle here:
2045 Unto no mete he him drough
Until his maister hadde eten ynough.
Him fayled ther bothe salt and breed,
And so him dide white wyne and reed;
But of swich thyng as they hadde,
2050 He and his leoun made hem glade.
The leoun hungred for the nones;
Ful faste he eet rawe flessh and bones.
Sir Ywayn in that ilke telde +
Leyde his heed upon his shelde;
2055 Al nyght the leoun aboute yede
To kepe his maister and his stede.
Thus the leoun and the knight
Lended + ther a fourtenyght.

On a day so it bifel,
2060 Sir Ywayn com unto the welle.
He saw the chapel and the thorn,
And seyde allas that he was born;
And whan he loked on the ston,
He fel in swonyng soon anon.
2065 As he fel, his swerd out-shook;
The pomel into the erthe took,
The poynt took unto his throte.
(Wel nere he made a sory note.)
Thurgh his armures soon it smot,
2070 A litel into his hals + it bot. +
And whan the leoun saw his blood,

2053 **that ilke telde** that same (tent-)covering.
2058 **Lended** remained.
2070 **hals** neck. **bot** bit.

He breyded+ as he hadde ben wood.
Than caste he up so lothly rerd,+
Ful many folk myghte he have ferd;
2075 He wende wel, so God me rede,
That his maister hadde ben dede.
It was ful greet pitee to here
What sorwe he made on his manere.
He stirte ful hertely, I you hete,+
2080 And took the swerd bitwixe his feet.
Up he sette it by a stane+
And ther he wolde himself have slayn;
And so he hadde soon, for certeyn,
But right in that ros Sir Ywayn;
2085 And as soon as he saw him stonde,
For fayn he likked foot and hond.
Sir Ywayn seyde oft-sithes, "Allas,
Of al-kyn men hard is my grace.
My lemman sette me certeyn day,
2090 And I it brak, so weylawey!
Allas, for dol how may I dwelle
To see this chapel and this welle,
Hir faire thorn, hir riche ston?
My gode dayes ben now al gon,
2095 My joye is don now al bidene+—
I am noght worthy to be sene.
I saw this wilde beste was ful bayn+
For my love himself have slayn.
Than sholde I, certes, by more right,
2100 Slee myself for swich a wight

2072 **breyded** roared, (?) drew back.
2073 **rerd** loud voice.
2079 **hete** promise.
2081 **stane** = *ston(e)*.
2095 **al bidene** all at once, entirely.
2097 **bayn** eager.

That I have for my folye lorn.
Allas the while that I was born!"

As Sir Ywayn made his mone,
In the chapel ay was oon
2105 And herde his murnyng hoolly al
Thurgh a crevace of the wal,
And soon it seyde wyth simple chere,
"'What artow, that murneth here?"
"A man," he seyde, "som-tyme+ I was.
2110 What artow? Tel me er I passe."
"'I am," it seyde, "the sorieste wight
That evere lyvde by day or nyght."
"Nay," he seyde, "by Seint Martine,
Ther is no sorwe mete+ to myne,
2115 Ne no wight so wyl of wane.+
I was a man, now am I nane;+
Whilom I was a noble knight
And a man of muchel myght;
I hadde knightes of my meynee
2120 And of richesse greet plentee;
I hadde a ful faire seignorye,+
And al I lost for my folye.
My moste sorwe, as shaltow here,
I lost a lady that was me dere."
2125   That other seyde, "Allas, allas,
Myn is a wel sorier cas:
To-morne I moot bere my jewyse+
As my fomen wol devise."

2109 **som-tyme** one time, formerly
2114 **mete** equal.
2115 **wyl of wane** i.e., homeless.
2116 **nane** = *non.*
2121 **seignorye** domain.
2127 **jewyse** judgment.

"Allas," he seyde, "what is the skile?"+
2130 "That shaltow here, Sire, if thou wyl.+
I was a mayden muchel of pride
Wyth a lady heer nere-biside;
Men me bicalle+ of tresoun,
And have me put heer in prisoun;
2135 I have no man to defende me:
Ther-fore to-morne brent moot I be."
He seyde, "What if thou getest a knight
That for thee wyth thy fos wyl fighte?"
"Sire," she seyde, "as moot I go,
2140 In this lond ben but knightes two
That me wolde helpe to cover+ of care:
That oon is went I wot noght whare;+
That other is dwellynge wyth the kyng
And wot noght of my myslikyng.+
2145 That oon of hem hot+ Sir Gawayn,
And that other hot Sir Ywayn.
For him shal I be don to dede
To-morne right in this same stede.
He is the kynges sone Urien."
2150 "Parfay," he seyde, " I have him seen;
I am he, and for my gilt
Shaltow nevere more be spilt.+
Thou art Lunete, if I can rede,
That helped me in muchel drede;
2155 I hadde ben deed, haddest thou noght ben.
Ther-fore tel me us bitwene

2129 **skile** reason.
2130 **wyl** = *wylt.*
2133 **bicalle** charge.
2141 **cover** recover.
2142 **whare** = *wher.*
2144 **myslikyng** trouble.
2145 **hot** is called.
2152 **spilt** destroyed.

How bicalle they thee of tresoun,
Thus for-to slee, and for what resoun."
    "Sire, they seye that my lady
2160 Lovede me moste specially,
And wroghte al after my rede:
Ther-fore they hate me to the dede.+
The styward seyth that don have I
Greet tresoun unto my lady.
2165 His two brether seyde it als,+
And I wiste that they seyde fals;
And soon I answerde as a sot+—
For foles bolt is sone shot—+
I seyde that I sholde fynde a knight
2170 That sholde me mayntene in my right
And fighte wyth hem alle three;
Thus the bataile wagede we.
Than they grauntede me as tite+
Fourty dayes unto respite;
2175 And at the kynges court I was:
I fond no confort ne no solas
Nother of knight, knave, ne swayn."
Than seyde he, "Wher was Sir Gawayn?
He hath ben evere trewe and lele+—
2180 He fayled nevere no damysel."
        She seyde, " In court he was noght sene,
For a knight ledde awey the quene;
The kyng ther-fore is swithe grym.
Sir Gawayn folwed after him;
2185 He cometh noght home, for certeyn,

2162 **dede** = *deeth*.
2165 **als** = *also*.
2167 **sot** madman.
2168 **foles bolt is sone shot** (a) fool's bolt is soon shot.
2173 **as tite** immediately.
2179 **lele** faithful.

Until he brynge the quene ageyn.
Now hast thou herde, so God me rede,
Why I shal be don to dede."
He seyde, "As I am trewe knight,
2190   I shal be redy for-to fighte
To-morne wyth hem alle three,
Lemman, for the love of thee.
At my myght I shal noght fayle;
But how so beth+ of the bataile,
2195   If any man my name thee frayne,+
On al manere loke thou it layne:+
Unto no man my name thou sey."
"Sire," she seyde, "for sothe, nay.
I preye to greet God alweldand+
2200   That they have noght the heigher hond;
Sith that ye wol my murnyng mende,
I take the grace that God wyl sende."
Sir Ywayn seyde, "I shal thee highte+
To mende thy murnyng at my myght;
2205   Thurgh grace of God in trinitee,
I shal thee wreke of hem alle three."

Than rod he forth into frith,
And his leoun went him wyth.
Hadde he riden but a stounde,
2210   A ful faire castel he founde;+
And Sir Ywayn, the sooth to seye,
Unto the castel took his weye.
Whan he cam at the castel yate,

2194 **beth** (it shall) be.
2195 **frayne** inquire (of).
2196 **layne** conceal.
2199 **alweldand** all-wielding.
2203 **highte** promise.
2210 **founde** = *fond* found.

Foure porters he fond ther-at.
2215 The drawe-brigge soon lette they doun,
But alle they fledde for the leoun,
They seyde, "Sire, wythouten doute,
That beste bihoveth thee leve ther-oute."
He seyde, "Sires, so have I wynne,+
2220 My leoun and I shulle noght twynne;+
I love him as wel, I you hete,+
As myself at one mete;+
Either shulle we samen+ lende,+
Or elles wol we hennes wende."
2225 But right wyth that the lord he mette—
And ful gladly he him grette—
Wyth knightes and squiers greet plentee,
And faire ladies and maydens free;
Ful muchel joye of him they made,
2230 But sorwe in her hertes they hadde.
Unto a chambre was he ledde
And unarmed and sithen cledde
In clothes that were gay and dere.
But ofte-tymes chaunged her chere;
2235 Som-tyme, he saw, they wepede alle
As they wolde to water falle;
They made swich murnyng and swich mone,
That gretter saw he nevere non;
They feynede hem ofte for his sake
2240 Faire semblaunt for-to make.
Ful greet wonder Sir Ywayn hadde
For they swich joye and sorwe made;
"Sire," he seyde, "if youre wyl ware,+

2219 **wynne** bliss, joy.
2220 **twynne** part.
2221 **hete** assure.
2222 **at one mete** i.e., equally.
2223 **samen** together. **lende** remain.
2243 **ware** = *were* (it) were.

I wolde wite why ye make swich care."

2245   "This joye," he seyde, "that we make now,
Sire, is al for we have you;
And, Sire, also we make this sorwe
For dedes that shulle be don to-morwe.
A geaunt woneth+ heer nere-biside,

2250   That is a devil of muchel pride:
His name hot+ Harpyns of Mountayne.
For him we lyve in muchel peyne:
My londes hath he robbed and reft;
Noght but this castel is me left.

2255   And, by God that in hevene wones,+
Sire, I hadde six knightes to sones:
I saw myself the two slough he,
To-morne the foure als slayn moot be—
He hath alle in his prisoun—

2260   And, Sire, for non other enchesoun+
But for I warned+ him to wyve
My doghter, fairest fode+ alyve.
Ther-fore is he wonder wroth,
And depely hath he sworn his oth

2265   Wyth maistrye+ that he shal hire wynne
And that the laddes of his kichinne
And also that his worste foot-knave
His wyl of that womman shal have,
But I to-morne myghte fynde a knight

2270   That durste wyth himselven fighte;
And I have non to him to go:
What wonder is if me be wo?"

2249 **woneth** dwells.
2251 **hot** is called.
2255 **wones** = *woneth.*
2260 **enchesoun** reason.
2261 **warned** refused.
2262 **fode** creature.
2265 **maistrye** superiority (in combat).

Sir Ywayn listned him ful wel,
And whan he hadde told ilke deel,
2275 "Sire," he seyde, "me think'th merveil
That ye soghte nevere no counseil
At the kynges hous heer-biside;
For certes, in al this world so wide
Is no man of so muchel myght,
2280 Geaunt, champioun, ne knight,
That he ne hath knightes of his meynee
That ful glade and blithe wolde be
For-to mete wyth swich a man
That they myghte kithe+ her myghtes on."
2285 He seyde, "Sire, so God me mende,
Unto the kynges court I sende+
To seche my maister Sir Gawayn;
For he wolde socoure me ful fayn.
He wolde noght leve for love ne drede,
2290 Hadde he wiste now of my nede;
For his suster is my wyf,
And he loveth hire as his lyf.
But a knight this othre day,
They tolde, hath led the quene awey;
2295 For-to seche hire went Sir Gawayn,
And yet ne cometh he noght ageyn."
Than Sir Ywayn siked+ sore,
And seyde unto the knight right thore,+
"Sire," he seyde, "for Gawayn sake
2300 This bataile wyl I undertake
For-to fighte wyth the geaunt;
And that upon swich a covenaunt,
If he come at swich a tyme,

2284 **kithe** make known, show.
2286 **sende** = *sente*.
2297 **siked** sighed.
2298 **thore** = *ther*.

So that we mowe fighte by pryme.+
2305 No lenger may I tente+ ther-to,
For other thyng I have to do:
I have a dede that moot be don
To-morne nedes bifore the noon."+
The knight sore sikynge seyde him til,+
2310 "Sire, God yelde thee thy gode wyl";
And alle that were ther in the halle
On knees bifore him gan they falle.
Forth ther cam a burde+ ful bright,
The faireste man myghte see in sight;
2315 Hir moder cam wyth hire y-fere,+
And bothe they murnde and made il+ chere.
The knight seyde, "Lo, verrayment,+
God hath us good socour sent:
This knight that of his grace wyl graunte
2320 For-to fighte wyth the geaunt."
On knees they felle doun to his feet
And thonkede him wyth wordes swete.
"A, God forbede," seyde Sir Ywayn,
"That the suster of Sir Gawayn
2325 Or any other of his blood born
Sholde on this wyse knele me biforn."
He took hem up tite bothe y-fere,
And preyde hem to amende her chere:
"And preyeth faste to God also
2330 That I may venge you on youre fo,
And that he come swich tyme of day

2304 **pryme** midmorning.
2305 **tente** attend.
2308 **noon** midday.
2309 **til** = *to*.
2313 **burde** lady, damsel.
2315 **wyth hire y-fere** together with her.
2316 **il** grievous.
2317 **verrayment** truly, indeed.

That I by-tyme+ may wende my weye
For-to do an other dede;
For, certes, thider moot I nede.
2335 Certes, I wolde noght hem biswike+
For-to wynne this kynges rike."+
(His thoght was on that damysel
That he lefte in the chapel.)
They seyde, "He is of greet renoun,
2340 For wyth him dwelleth the leoun."
Ful wel conforted were they alle,
Bothe in boure and als in halle;
Ful glade were they of her gest;
And whan tyme was to go to reste,
2345 The lady broghte him to his bed;
And for the leoun she was adred.
No man durste neighe+ his chambre nere,
From they were broght ther-inne y-fere.

Soon at morne, whan it was day,
2350 The lady and the faire may
To Ywayn chambre wente they soon,
And the dore they have undon.
Sir Ywayn to the chirche yede
Er he dide any other dede;
2355 He herde the servise of the day,
And sithen to the knight gan seye,
"Sire," he seyde, "now moot I wende,
Lenger heer dar I noght lende:+
To other place bihoveth me fare."
2360 Than hadde the knight ful muchel care;

2332 **by-tyme** in (good) time.
2335 **biswike** betray.
2336 **rike** realm.
2347 **neighe** (to) near, come close to.
2358 **lende** remain.

223

He seyde, "Sire, dwelleth a litel throwe +
For love of Gawayn that ye knowe;
Socour us now er ye wende.
I shal you yeve wythouten ende
2365 Half my lond wyth toun and tour,
And ye wol helpe us in this stour." +
Sir Ywayn seyde, "Nay, God forbede
That I sholde take any mede." +
Than was greet dol, so God me gladde,
2370 To see the sorwe that they made.
Of hem Sir Ywayn hadde greet pitee—
Him thoghte his herte myghte breke in three;
For in greet drede ay gan he dwelle
For the mayden in the chapel;
2375 For, certes, if she were don to dede, +
Of him were than non other rede
But either he sholde himselven slo, +
Or wood ageyn to the wode go.
Right wyth that ther cam a grome +
2380 And seyde hem that geaunt come:
"Youre sones bryngeth he him biforn
Wel nere naked as they were born."
Wyth wrecched ragges were they clad,
And faste bounden, thus ben they led.
2385 The geaunt was bothe large and long,
And bar a levour + of iren ful strong;
Ther-wyth he bette hem bittrely;
Greet routhe it was to here hem crie:

2361 **litel throwe** short time.
2366 **stour** conflict.
2368 **mede** reward, compensation.
2375 **dede** = *deeth.*
2377 **slo** = *slee.*
2379 **grome** servant, man.
2386 **levour** pole.

They hadde no-thyng hem for-to hide.
2390 A dwergh+ yede on that other side;
He bar a scourge wyth cordes ten;
Ther-wyth he bette tho gentil men
Evere anon as he were wood:
After ilke bond+ brast out the blood.
2395 And whan they at the walles were,
He cried loude that men myghte here,
"If thou wylt have thy sones in hele,+
Deliver me that damysel.
I shal hire yeve to warisoun+
2400 Oon of the fouleste quisteroun+
That evere yet eet any breed;
He shal have hir maydenhede.
Ther shal non other lie hire by
But naked harlotes+ and lousy.
2405 Whan the lord thise wordes herde,
As he were wood for wo he ferde.
Sir Ywayn than that was curteis
Unto the knight ful soon he seys:+
"This geaunt is ful fiers and fell+
2410 And of his wordes ful cruel;
I shal delivere hire of his owe,+
Or elles be deed wythin a throwe.+
For certes it were a mysaventure
That so gentil a creature

2390 **dwergh** dwarf.
2394 **bond** stroke.
2397 **hele** sound condition.
2399 **to warisoun** as reward, prize.
2400 **quisteroun** low-born person.
2404 **harlotes** rascals.
2408 **seys** = *seyth.*
2409 **fiers and fell** fierce and deadly.
2411 **owe** power.
2412 **throwe** (short) time.

2415 Sholde evere so foule hap bifalle
      To be defouled wyth a thralle."+
          Soon was he armed, Sir Ywayn;
      Ther-fore the ladies wer ful fayn.
      They helped to lace him in his wede,
2420 And soon he leep upon his stede.
      They preye to God that grace him graunte
      For-to slee that foule geaunt.
      The drawe-brigges were leten doun,
      And forth he rideth wyth his leoun.
2425 Ful many sory murnynge man
      Lefte he in the castel than
      That on her knees to God of myght
      Preyde ful hertely for the knight.
          Sir Ywayn rod into the playn,
2430 And the geaunt cam him ageyn.
      His levour+ was ful greet and long
      And himself ful muchel and strong.
      He seyde, "What devil made thee so bold
      For-to come hider out of thy hold ?
2435 Whoso evere thee hider send+
      Lovede thee litel, so God me mende;
      Of thee he wolde be wroken fayn."
      "Do forth thy beste," seyde Sir Ywayn.
      Al the armure he was in
2440 Was noght but of a bul-skyn.
      Sir Ywayn was to him ful prest:+
      He strok to him in-middes the brest;
      The spere was bothe stif and good—
      Wher it took bit,+ outbrast the blood;

2416 **thralle** slave.
2429 **levour** pole, bar.
2435 **send** = *sente.*
2441 **prest** prepared, prompt.
2444 **Wher it took bit** where it struck.

2445   So faste Sir Ywayn on it soghte
       The bul-skyn avayled noght.
       The geaunt stumbled wyth the dynt,+
       And unto Sir Ywayn he mynte,+
       And on the sheeld he hit ful faste—
2450   It was a merveil that it mighte laste.
       The levour bended ther-wythal,
       Wyth greet fors he lett it falle;
       The geaunt was so strong a wight
       That nevere for no dynt of knight
2455   Ne for bataile that he sholde make,
       Wolde he non other wepen take.
       Sir Ywayn lefte his spere of hond
       And strok aboute him wyth his brond,+
       And the geaunt muchel of mayn
2460   Strok ful faste to him ageyn,
       Til atte laste, wythin a throwe,
       He rest him on his sadel-bowe;
       And that perceived his leoun,
       That his heved+ so heng doun,
2465   He hoped+ that his lord was hirt+
       And to the geaunt soon he stirte.
       The skyn and flessh bothe rof+ he doun
       From his hals+ to his cropoun;+
       His rybbes myghte men see anon,
2470   For al was bare unto bon.
       At the leoun ofte he mynte,
       But evere he lepeth from his dynt

2447 **dynt** stroke, blow.
2448 **mynte** aimed a blow.
2458 **brond** sword.
2464 **heved** = *heed* head.
2465 **hoped** thought. **hirt** = *hurt*.
2467 **rof** tore.
2468 **hals** neck. **cropoun** buttocks.

So that no strok on him light.
By than was Ywayn come to myght,
2475 Than wyl he wreke him if he may.
The geaunt yaf he ful good pay:
He smot awey al his lefte cheke,
His shulder als of gan he cleke[+]
That bothe his levour and his hond
2480 Felle doun lowe upon the lond.
Sithen wyth a strok to him he stirte
And smot the geaunt unto the herte.
Than was non other tale to telle,
But faste unto the erthe he fel,
2485 As it hadde ben a hevy tree.
        Than myghte men in the castel see
Ful muchel myrthe on ilke side.
The yates caste they open wide;
The lord unto Sir Ywayn ran,
2490 Him folwed many a joyeful man;
Also the lady ran ful faste
And hir doghter was noght the laste.
I may noght telle the joye they hadde;
And the four brether were ful glade,
2495 For they were out of bale broght.
The lord wiste it helped noght
To preye Sir Ywayn for-to dwelle,
For tales that he bifore gan telle;
But hertely wyth his myght and mayn
2500 He preyde him for-to come ageyn
And dwelle wyth him a litel stage,[+]
Whan he hadde don his vassage.[+]
He seyde, "Sire, that may I noght do;

2478 **cleke** to pull.
2501 **stage** period of time.
2502 **vassage** vassal's deeds.

Bileveth wel, for me bus+ go."
2505 Hem was ful wo he wolde noght dwelle,
But fayn they were that it so fel.

The nigheste weye than gan he wele+
Until he cam to the chapel.
Ther he fond a muchel fyr;
2510 And the mayden wyth lilye lire+
In hir smok was bounden faste
Into the fyr for-to be caste.
Unto himself he seyde in hye
And preyde to God almyghty
2515 That he sholde for his muchel myght
Save from shame that swete wight.
"If they be many and muchel of pris,
I shal lete for no cowardise;
For wyth me is bothe God and right
2520 And they shulle helpe me for-to fighte,
And my leoun shal helpe me:
Than ben we foure ayeins hem three."
Sir Ywayn rideth and crieth then,+
"Abideth, I bidde you, false men!
2525 It semeth wel that ye ben wode
That wol spille this sakles+ blood.
Ye shulle noght so, if that I may."
His leoun made him redy weye.
Naked he saw the mayden stonde,
2530 Bihynde hire bounden either hond;
Than siked Ywayn wonder ofte,
Unethes+ myghte he sitte a-lofte.

2504 **me bus** (it) behooves me (to).
2507 **wele** choose.
2510 **lilye lire** lily(-like) flesh.
2523 **then** = *than*.
2526 **sakles** innocent.
2532 **Unethes** hardly.

Ther was no semblaunt hem bitwene
That evere either hadde other sene.
2535 Al aboute hire myghte men see
Ful muchel sorwe and greet pitee
Of othre ladies that ther were
Wepynge wyth ful sory chere.
"Lord," they seyde, "what is oure gilt?
2540 Oure joye, oure confort shal be spilt.
Who shal now oure erandes[+] seye?
Allas, who shal now for us preye?"
Whil they thus carpede was Lunete
On knees bifore the preest set
2545 Of hir synnes hire for-to shrive.
And unto hire he wente blive,[+]
Hir hond he took, and up she ros;
"Lemman," he seyde, "wher ben thise fos?"
"Sire, lo hem yonder in yon stede
2550 Bidynge until I be dede.
They have demde[+] me wyth wronge[+]—
Wel nere hadde ye dwelt over-longe—
I preye to God He do you mede
That ye wolde helpe me in this nede."
2555 Thise wordes herde than the styward;
He hyeth him unto hire ful harde.
He seyde, "Thou liest, fals woman!
For thy tresoun artow tane.
She hath bitrayed hir lady,
2560 And, Sire, so wyl she thee in hy.
And ther-fore, Sire, by Goddes doom,
I rede thou wende right as thou cam:
Thou takest a ful feble rede[+]

2541 **erandes** messages, intercessions.
2546 **blive** quickly.
2551 **demde** judged. **wyth wronge** wrongfully.
2563 **feble rede** poor advice.

If thou for hire wylt suffre dede."+
2565   Unto the styward than seyde he,
"Whoso is feerd, I rede he flee;
And certes I have ben this day
Wher I hadde ful large pay.+
And yet," he seyde, " I shal noght fayle."
2570 To hem he waged the bataile.
"Do wey thy leoun," seyde the styward,
"For that is noght oure foreward.+
Allone shalt thou fighte wyth us three."
And unto him thus answerde he,
2575 "Of my leoun no help I crave.
I ne have non other fote-knave:
If he wyl do you any dere,+
I rede wel that ye you were."+
The styward seyde, "On al-kyn wyse
2580 Thy leoun, Sire, thou moot chastise
That he do heer no harm this day,
Or elles wend forth on thy weye;
For hir warant+ mayst thou noght be
But thou allone fighte wyth us three.
2585 Al thise men wite, and so wot I,
That she bitrayed hir lady.
As traitouresse shal she have hire—+
She shal be brent heer in this fyr."
Sir Ywayn seyde, "Nay, God forbede!"—
2590 He wiste wel how the sooth yede—
"I trowe to wreke hire wyth the beste."

2564 **dede** = *deeth.*
2568 **pay** satisfaction.
2572 **foreward** agreement.
2577 **dere** harm.
2578 **were** protect.
2583 **warant** defender, champion.
2587 **hire** reward, compensation.
2588 *shal* is supplied.

He bad his leoun go to reste;
And he lay him soon anon
Doun bifore hem everichoon;
2595 Bitwene his legges he leyde his tayl,
And so biheeld to the bataile.

Alle three they ride to Sir Ywayn,
And smertly rideth he hem ageyn;
In that tyme no-thyng tynte+ he,
2600 For his oon strok was worth heres three.
He strok the styward on the shelde
That he fel doun flat in the felde;
But up he ros yet atte laste
And to Sir Ywayn strok ful faste.
2605 Ther-at the leoun greved sore—
No lenger wolde he than lie thore;+
To helpe his maister he went anon,
And the ladies everichoon
That were ther for-to see that sight
2610 Preyde ful faste ay for the knight.
The leoun hasted him ful harde,
And soon he cam to the stywarde.
A ful fell mynt+ to him he made;
He bigan at the shulder-blade,
2615 And wyth his pawn al rof+ he doun
Bothe hauberk+ and his actoun+
And al the flessh doun to his knee,
So that men myghte his guttes see;
To grounde he fel so al to-rent+

2599 **tynte** wasted.
2606 **thore** = *ther*.
2613 **fell mynt** deadly strike.
2615 **rof** tore.
2616 **hauberk** breast armor. **actoun** jerkin.
2619 **al to-rent** torn to pieces.

232

2620 Was ther no man that him mente: +
Thus the leoun gan him slo. +
Than were they but two and two,
And certeynly ther Sir Ywayn
Als wyth wordes dide his mayn
2625 For-to chastise his leoun;
But he ne wolde no more lie doun.
The leoun thoghte, how so he seyde,
That wyth his help he was wel payde. +
They smite the leoun on ilke side
2630 And yeve him many woundes wide.
Whan that he saw his leoun blede,
He fered for wo as he wolde wede; +
And faste he strok than in that stour—
Myghte ther non his dyntes doure. +
2635 So grevously than he bigan,
That doun he bar bothe hors and man.
They yolde hem soon to Sir Ywayn,
And ther-of were the folk ful fayn;
And soon quitte to hem here hire, +
2640 For bothe he caste hem in the fyre,
And seyde, "Who juggeth men wyth wronge
The same juggement shulle they fonge." +
Thus he helped the mayden yinge, +
And sithen he made the saghtelyng +
2645 Bitwene hire and the riche lady.
Than al the folk ful hastily

2620 **mente** (?) pitied.
2621 **slo** = *slee.*
2628 **payde** pleased.
2632 **wede** become mad.
2634 **doure** endure.
2639 **quitte to hem here hire** gave them their due.
2642 **fonge** take, receive.
2643 **yinge** = *yonge.*
2644 **saghtelyng** agreement, peace.

Profrede hem to his servise
To worshipe him evere on alle wyse.
Non of hem alle wiste but Lunete

2650 That they wyth her lord were met.
The lady preyde him als the hende +
That he home wyth hem wolde wende
For-to sojourne ther a stounde,
Til he were warisshed + of his wounde.

2655 By his sore sette he noght a stra +
But for his leoun was him wa. +
"Madame," he seyde, "certes, nay,
I myghte noght dwelle, the sooth to seye."
She seyde, "Sire, sith thou wylt wende,

2660 Sey us thy name, so God thee mende."
"Madame," he seyde, "by Seint Simoun,
I hote + the knight wyth the leoun."
She seyde, "We sawe you nevere er now,
Ne nevere herde we speke of you."

2665 "Ther-by," he seyde, "ye understonde
I am noght knowen wide in londe."
She seyde, "I preye thee for-to dwelle,
If that thou mayst, heer us a-melle." +
If she hadde wist wel who it was,

2670 She wolde wel levere + have let him passe;
And ther-fore wolde he noght be knowen
Bothe for hir ese and for his owene.
He seyde, "No lenger dwelle I ne may;
Bileveth wel and haveth good day.

2651 **als the hende** courteously.
2654 **warisshed** recovered.
2655 **stra** straw, i.e., cared nothing.
2656 **wa** = *wo.*
2662 **hote** am called.
2669 **a-melle** among.
2670 **levere** sooner, rather.

234

2675   I preye to Crist, Hevene Kyng,
        Lady, lene+ you good lyvyng,
        And lene you grace that al youre anoye+
        May turne you unto muche joye."
        She seyde, "God graunte that it so be."
2680   Unto himself than thus seyde he,
        "Thou art the lok and keye also
        Of al my wele and al my wo."

        Now wendeth he forth and murnyng mase,+
        And non of hem wiste what he was,
2685   But Lunete that he bad sholde layne;+
        And so she dide wyth al hir mayne.
        She conveyed him forth on his weye:
        He seyde, "Gode lemman, I thee preye
        That thou telle to no moder sone
2690   Who hath ben thy champioun;
        And als I preye thee, swete wight,
        Late and erly+ thou do thy myght
        Wyth speche unto my lady free
        For-to make hire freend wyth me.
2695   Sith ye ben now togidre glade,
        Help thou that we were frendes made."
        "Certes, Sire," she seyde, "ful fayn
        Ther-aboute wyl I be bayn;+
        And that ye have don me this day,
2700   God do you mede, as He wel may."

        Of Lunete thus his leve he taketh,
        But in herte greet sorwe he hath.

2676 **lene** grant.
2677 **anoye** trouble, vexation.
2683 **mase** = *maketh.*
2685 **layne** conceal (it).
2692 **Late and erly** i.e., at all times.
2698 **bayn** eager.

His leoun feled so muchel wo
That he ne myghte no ferre go.
2705   Sir Ywayn puld gras in the felde
And made a couche upon his shelde;
Ther-on his leoun leyde he thore,+
And forth he rideth and siketh sore;
On his shelde so he him ledde,
2710   Than was he ful evil sted.+
Forth he rideth by frith and fel+
Til he cam to a faire castel.
Ther he called, and swithe soon
The porter hath the yates undon,
2715   And to him made he ful good chere.
He seyde, "Sire, ye ben welcome here."
Sir Ywayn seyde, "God do thee mede,
For ther-of have I muchel nede."
In he rod right at the yate;
2720   Faire folk kepte+ him ther-at.
They toke his sheeld and his leoun,
And ful softely they leyde it doun;
Some to stable ladde his stede,
And some also unlaced his wede.
2725   They tolde the lord than of that knight,
And soon he and his lady bright
And her sones and doghtres alle
Come ful faire him for-to calle;
They were ful fayn he ther was sted.
2730   To chambre soon they have him led;
His bed was ordeyned richely,
And his leoun they leyde him by;
Him was no mystere for-to crave+—

2707 **thore** = *ther.*
2710 **sted** bestead.
2711 **frith and fel** woodland and wasteland.
2720 **kepte** attended (to).
2733 **mystere for-to crave** need to ask (for).

Redy he hadde what he wolde have.
2735 Two maydens wyth him they lefte
That were wel lered of lechecraft;+
The lordes doghtres bothe they were
That were left to kepe him ther.
They helede him everich a wounde,
2740 And his leoun soon made they sounde.
I can not telle how longe he lay;
Whan he was heled he went his weye.

But whil he sojourned in that place,
In that lond bifel this cas.
2745 A litel thennes in a stede
A greet lord of the lond was dede.
Lyvynge he hadde non other aire+
But two doghtres that were ful faire.
As soon as he was leyd in molde+
2750 The elder suster seyde she wolde
Wende to court soon as she myghte,
For-to gete som doughty knight
For-to wynne hire al the lond
And holde it hoolly in hir hond.
2755 The yonger suster saw she ne myghte
Have that fel unto hir righte
But if that it were by bataile;
To court she wyl to axe counseil.
The elder suster soon was yare;+
2760 Unto the court faste gan she fare.
To Sir Gawayn she made hir mone,
And he hath graunted hire anon,
"But it bus+ be so prively

2736 **lered of lechecraft** instructed in medicine.
2747 **aire** heir.
2749 **molde** (the) earth.
2759 **yare** ready.
2763 **bus** must necessarily.

That non wot but thou and I.
2765 If thou of me makest any yelp,+
Lorn hast thou al myn help."
　　Than after on that other day,
Unto court cam that other may,+
And to Sir Gawayn soon she went
2770 And tolde unto him hir entente;
Of his help she him bisoghte.
"Certes," he seyde, "that may I noght."
Than she wepte and wrong hir handes;+
And right wyth that come newe tidandes,+
2775 How a knight wyth a leoun
Hadde slayn a geaunt ful feloun.+
The same knight ther tolde this tale
That Sir Ywayn broghte from bale
That hadde wedd Gawayn suster dere.
2780 She and hir sones were ther y-fere;
They broghte the dwergh,+ that be ye bolde,+
And to Sir Gawayn have they told
How the knight wyth the leoun
Delivred hem out of prisoun,
2785 And how he for Sir Gawayn sake
Gan that bataile undertake,
And als how nobly that he wroghte.
Sir Gawayn seyde, "I knowe him noght."
The yonger mayden than al soon
2790 Of the kyng axeth this boon,
To have respite of fourty dayes,
As it fel to londes layes.+
She wiste ther was no man of mayn

2765 **yelp** boast.
2768 **may** maiden.
2773 **handes** = *hondes.*
2774 **tidandes** = *tidynges.*
2776 **feloun** fierce, evil.
2781 **dwergh** dwarf. **bolde** assured.
2792 **layes** = *lawes.*

That wolde fighte wyth Sir Gawayn.
2795 She thoghte to seche by frith and fel
The knight that she herde hem of telle.
Respite was graunted of this thyng;
The mayden took leve at the kyng
And sithen at al the barounage,
2800 And forth she went on hir viage.+
 Day ne nyght wolde she noght spare;
Thurgh al the lond faste gan she fare
Thurgh castel and thurgh ilke toun
To seche the knight wyth the leoun:
2805 He helpeth alle in word and dede
That unto him have any nede.
She soghte him thurgh al that land,+
But of him herde she no tidand;+
No man coude telle hire wher he was:
2810 Ful greet sorwe in herte she has.+
So muchel murnyng gan she make
That a greet siknesse gan she take.
But in hir weye right wel she spedde;
At that castel was she sted
2815 Wher Sir Ywayn er hadde ben
Heled of his siknesse clene.+
Ther she was ful wel knowen
And as welcome as to hir owene;
Wyth al-kyn gamen they gonne hire gladde,
2820 And muchel joye of hire they made.
Unto the lord she tolde hir cas,
And helpyng hastily she has.+

2800 **viage** journey, undertaking.
2807 **land** = *lond.*
2808 **tidand** = *tidying.*
2810 **has** = *hath.*
2816 **clene** entirely.
2822 **has** = *hath.*

Stille in lechyng⁺ ther she lay;
A mayden for hire took the weye
2825 For-to seche if that she myghte
In any londe here of that knight;
And that same castel cam she by
Wher Ywayn wedded the lady.
And faste she spired⁺ in ech sesoun⁺
2830 After the knight wyth the leoun.
They tolde hire how he went hem fro,
And also how they sawe him slo⁺
Three noble knightes for the nones
That foghte wyth him al at ones.
2835 She seyde, "Par charitee, I you preye,
If that ye wite, wol ye me seye
Whider-ward that he is went?"
They seyde, for sothe, they toke no tente;⁺
"Ne heer is non that thee can telle,
2840 But if it be a damysel
For whos sake he hider cam,
And for hire the bataile he nam.
We trowe wel that she can thee wisse;⁺
Yonder in yon chirche she is.
2845 Ther-fore we rede to hire thou go;"
And hastily than dide she so.
Either other ful goodly grette,
And soon she frayned⁺ at Lunete
If she coude any certeyn seyn;
2850 And hendely answerde she ageyn,
"I shal sadel my palfrey

2823 **lechyng** medical treatment.
2829 **spired** inquired. **ech sesoun** due time.
2832 **slo** = *slee.*
2838 **tente** notice.
2843 **wisse** direct.
2848 **frayned** inquired.

And wende wyth thee forth on thy weye
And wisse thee as wel as I can."
Ful ofte-sithes thonked she hire than.
2855   Lunete was ful smertly yare,+
And wyth the mayden forth gan she fare.
As they wente, al she hire tolde,
How she was taken and don in holde,
How wikkedly that she was wreyed,+
2860   And how that traitours on hire leyed,+
And how that she sholde have ben brent
Hadde noght God hire socour sent
Of that knight wyth the leoun—
"He lesed+ me out of prisoun."
2865   She broghte hire soon into a playn,
Wher she parted from Sir Ywayn;
She seyde, "No more can I telle thee,
But heer parted he from me.
How that he went wot I no more,
2870   But wounded was he wonder sore.
God that for us suffred wounde
Lene+ us to see him hol and sounde.
No lenger wyth thee may I dwelle;
But comly+ Crist that heried+ helle
2875   Lene the grace that thou may spede+
Of thyn erand as thou hast nede."
Lunete hastily hyeth hire hom,
And the mayden soon to the castel cam
Wher he was heled bifore-hond.

2855 **yare** ready.
2859 **wreyed** charged.
2860 **leyed** accused.
2864 **lesed** set free.
2872 **Lene** give, grant.
2874 **comly** fair. **heried** harried.
2875 **spede** succeed, prosper.

2880   The lord soon at the yate she fond
        Wyth knightes and ladies greet companye;
        She haylsed⁺ hem alle ful hendely,
        And ful faire preyde she to hem than,
        If they coude they sholde hire can⁺
2885   Wher she myghte fynde, in tour or toun,
        A comly knight wyth a leoun.
        Than seyde the lord, "By swete Jhesus,
        Right now parted he from us;
        Lo, heer the steppes of his stede—
2890   Evene unto him they wol thee lede."
          Than took she leve and went hir weye,
        Wyth spores she spared noght hir palfrey;
        Faste she hyed wyth al hir myght
        Until she of him hadde a sight,
2895   And of his leoun that by him ran.
        Wonder joyeful was she than,
        And wyth hir hors she hasted so faste
        That she overtook him atte laste.
        She haylsed him wyth herte ful fayn,
2900   And he hire haylsed faire ageyn.
        She seyde, "Sire, wide have I you soght;
        And for my self ne is it noght,
        But for a damysel of pris
        That holden is⁺ bothe war and wys.
2905   Men don to hire ful greet outrage—
        They wolde hire reve⁺ hir heritage;
        And in this londe now lyveth non
        That she trusteth hire upon,
        But only upon God and thee,

2882 **haylsed** greeted.
2884 **can** make known (to).
2904 **That holden is** i.e., who is held to be.
2906 **reve** rob (of).

2910   For thou art of so greet bountee;+
        Thurgh help of thee she hopeth wel
        To wynne hir right everich a deel.+
        She seyth no knight that lyveth now
        May helpe hire half so wel as thou;
2915   Greet word shal gon of thy vassage+
        If that thou wynne hir heritage.
        For thoght she took swich siknesse sore,
        So that she myghte travaile no more;
        I have you soght on sides sere:+
2920   Ther-fore youre answere wolde I here—
        Whether ye wol wyth me wende,
        Or elles-wher you liketh to lende."
        He seyde, "That knight that idel lies+
        Ofte-sithes wynneth ful litel pries.+
2925   For-thy my rede shal soon be tane:
        Gladly wyth thee wyl I gane+
        Whider-so thou wylt me lede,
        And hertely helpe thee in thy nede.
        Sith thou hast me so wide soght,
2930   Certes, fayle thee shal I noght."

        Thus her weye forth gonne they halde+
        Unto a castel that was cald+
        The Castel of Hevy Sorwe.
        Ther wolde he bide until the morwe:

2910 **bountee** virtue, excellence.
2912 **everich a deel** altogether, completely.
2915 **vassage** prowess.
2919 **sere** several, various.
2923 **lies** = *lieth.*
2924 **pries** = *pris.*
2926 **gane** = *go(n).*
2931 **halde** = *holde.*
2932 **cald** = *called.*

2935 Ther to abide him thoghte it beste,
For the sonne drough faste to reste.
But alle the men that they mette
Greet wonder soon of hem they sette,
And seyde, "Thou wrecche, unsely+ man,
2940 Why wylt thou heer thyn herber+ tane?
Thou passest noght wythoute despite."
Sir Ywayn answerde hem as tite+
And seyde, "For sothe, ye ben unhende
An uncouth+ man so for-to shende;+
2945 Ye sholde noght seye him vilanye
But if ye wiste enchesoun+ why."
They answerde than and seyde ful soon,
"Thou shalt wite er to-morne at noon."
Sir Ywayn seyde, "For al youre sawe+
2950 Unto yon castel wyl I drawe."
He and his leoun and the may
Unto the castel toke the weye.
Whan the porter of hem hadde sight,
Soon he seyde unto the knight,
2955 "Cometh forth," he seyde, "ye alle togidre!
Ful ille hayle+ ben ye come hider."
Thus were they welcomed at the yate,
And yet they wente al in ther-at;
Unto the porter no word they seyde.
2960 A halle they founde ful goodly grayed;+
And as Sir Ywayn made entree,
Faste biside him than saw he

2939 **unsely** unfortunate.
2940 **herber** harbor, lodging.
2942 **as tite** quickly.
2944 **uncouth** strange. **shende** reproach.
2946 **enchesoun** reason, cause.
2949 **sawe** saying
2956 **ille hayle** unfortunately.
2960 **grayed** adorned, prepared.

A propre place and faire, y-wis,
Enclosed aboute wyth a palis.+
2965 He loked in bitwixe the trees+
And many maydens ther he sees+
Werkynge silk and gold-wire;
But they were alle in poure atire.
Her clothes were riven on yvel array;+
2970 Ful tendrely alle wepede they.
Her face were lene and als unclene,
And blake smokkes hadde they on bidene;
They hadde myschiefs+ ful many-fold
Of hunger, of thurst, and of cold;
2975 And evere anon they wepede alle
As they wolde to water falle.
    Whan Ywayn al this understood,
Ageyn unto the yates he yood;+
But they were sparred+ ferly+ faste
2980 Wyth lokkes that ful wel wolde laste.
The porter keped hem wyth his mayn,
And seyde, "Sire, thou most wende ageyn;
I wot thou wolde out at the yate,
But thou mayst noght by no gate.+
2985 Thy herber is take til to-morwe,
And ther-fore getest thou muchel sorwe.
Among thy fos heer sted artow."
He seyde, "So have I ben er now
And passed ful wel: so shal I here.

2964 **palis** palisade.
2965 **trees** stakes (of the palisade).
2966 **sees** = *seeth*.
2969 **riven on yvel array** torn (so as to be) in terrible condition.
2973 **myschiefs** troubles, misfortunes.
2978 **yood** = *yede* went.
2979 **sparred** fastened. **ferly** wondrously.
2984 **gate** way.

2990 But leve freend, wyltow me lere+
Of thise maydens what they are,
That werke al this riche ware?"+
He seyde, "If thou wylt wite trewely,
Forther-more thou most aspye."
2995 "Ther-fore," he seyde, "I shal noght lete."+
He soghte and fond a derne+ wiket,
He opened it and in he yede.
"Maydens," he seyde, "God moot you spede,
And as He suffred woundes sare,+
3000 He sende you coveryng+ of youre care
So that ye myghte make myrier chere."
"Sire," they seyde, "God yef so were!"+
"Youre sorwe," he seyde, "unto me seye,
And I shal mende it, if I may."
3005 Oon of hem answerde ageyn
And seyde, "The sooth we shulle noght layne;+
We shulle you telle er ye go ferre
Why we ben heer and what we ere.+
Sire, ye shulle understonde
3010 That we ben alle of Maydenlond.
Oure kyng upon his jolitee
Passed thurgh many contree
Auntures to spire+ and to spye
For-to assaye his owene body.

2990 **lere** inform, teach.
2992 **ware** goods, wares.
2995 **lete** fail.
2996 **derne** secret.
2999 **sare** = *sore*.
3000 **coveryng** recovery.
3002 **God yef so were** God grant it should be so.
3006 **layne** conceal.
3008 **ere** are.
3013 **spire** inquire (out). Second *to* is supplied.

3015 His herber heer ones gan he ta:⁺
That was bigynnyng of oure wa.⁺
For heer-inne ben two champiouns;
Men seyn they ben the devil sones
Geten of a womman wyth a ram;
3020 Ful many man have they don gram.⁺
What knight herbereth heer a nyght,
Wyth bothe at ones bihoveth him fighte.
So bus⁺ thee do, by belle and book:
Allas, that thou thyn inn heer took.⁺
3025 Oure kyng has wight himself to welde⁺
And of fourtene yeres of elde
Whan he was take wyth hem to fighte;
But unto hem hadde he no myght,
And whan he saw him bud be dede,⁺
3030 Than he couthe no bettre rede,
But dide him hoolly in her grace,
And made hem seurtee⁺ in that place
For-to yelde hem ilke yere,
So that he sholde be hol and fere,⁺
3035 Thritty maydens to trowage,⁺
And alle sholde be of heigh parage⁺
And the farieste of his lond;
Heer-to heeld he up his hond.

3015 **ta** = *take.*
3016 **wa** = *wo.*
3020 **gram** harm, hostility.
3023 **bus** (it) behooves.
3024 **took** = *toke.*
3025 **wight himself to welde** (?) swift to rule himself.
3029 **him bud be dede** i.e., that he would be killed.
3032 **seurtee** surety.
3034 **hol and fere** sound.
3035 **trowage** tribute.
3036 **parage** birth, lineage.

This ilke rent bihoveth him gyve⁺
3040   As longe as the fendes⁺ lyve,
Or til they ben in bataile tane,
Or elles until they ben al slayn.
Than shulle we passe al hennes quite,⁺
That heer suffren al this despite.⁺
3045   But heer-of is noght for-to speke;
Is non in world that us may wreke.
We werke wyth silver, silk, and gold—
Is non richer on this molde—⁺
And nevere the bettre ben we cled,
3050   And in greet hunger ben we sted;
For al that we werke in this stede,
We have noght half oure fille of breed;
For the beste that seweth heer any stik⁺
Taketh but foure pens⁺ in a wik;⁺
3055   And that is litel who som taketh hede
Any of us to clothe and fede.
Echoon of us, wythoute lesyng,⁺
Myghte wynne ech wik fourty shilyng;
And yet, but if we travaile more,
3060   Ofte they bete us wonder sore.
It helpeth noght to telle this tale,
For ther beth nevere boot⁺ of oure bale.⁺
Oure moste sorwe, sith we bigan,⁺
That is that we see many a man,

3039 **gyve** = *yeve* give.
3040 **fendes** (?) devils.
3043 **quite** free.
3044 **despite** injury, cruelty.
3048 **molde** earth.
3053 **stik** stitch.
3054 **pens** pence. **wik** week.
3057 **lesyng** lying, deceit.
3062 **boot** redress. **bale** sorrow.
3063 **bigan** = *bigonne.*

3065   Doughty dukes, erles, and barouns,
       Ofte-sithes slayn wyth thise champiouns.
       Wyth hem to-morne bihoveth thee fighte."
       Sir Ywayn seyde, "God, most of myght,
       Shal strengthe me in ilke dede
3070   Ayeins tho devils and al her drede;
       That lord delivere you of youre fos."
       Thus taketh he leve and forth he gos.+

       He passed forth into the halle.
       Ther fond he no man him to calle;
3075   No beautesse+ wolde they to him bede,+
       But hastily they toke his stede
       And also the maydens palfrey,
       Were servde wel wyt corn and hay,
       For wel they hopede that Sir Ywayn
3080   Sholde nevere have had his stede ageyn.
       Thurgh the halle Sir Ywayn gas+
       Into oon orcherd playne pas;+
       His mayden wyth him ledeth he.
       He fond a knight under a tree:
3085   Upon a cloth of gold he lay.
       Bifore him sat a ful faire may;
       A lady sat wyth hem y-fere.
       The mayden radde+ that they myghte here
       A real+ romaunce in that place;
3090   But I ne wot of whom it was.
       She was but fiftene yeres old;

3072 **gos** = *goth.*
3075 **beautesse** courtesy. **bede** offer.
3081 **gas** = *goth.*
3082 **playne pas** i.e., quickly.
3088 **radde** read.
3089 **real** royal.

The knight was lord of al that hold,+
And the mayden was his aire;+
She was bothe gracious, good, and faire.
3095   Soon, whan they sawe Sir Ywayn,
Smertly rise they him ageyn,
And by the hond the lord him taketh,
And unto him greet myrthe he maketh.
He seyde, "Sire, by swete Jhesus,
3100   Thou art ful welcome unto us."
The mayden was buxom and bayn+
For-to unarme Sir Ywayn;
Serk and breke+ bothe she him broghte,
That ful craftily were wroght
3105   Of riche cloth softe as the silk,
And ther-to white as any milk.
She broghte him ful riche wedes to were,+
Hose and shoos and al-kyn gere.
She peyned hire wyth al hir myght
3110   To serve him and his mayden bright.
Soon they went in to soupere:
Ful royally servde they were
Wyth metes and drynkes of the beste,
And sithen were they broght to reste.
3115   In his chambre by him laye
His owene leoun and his may.
    At morne, whan it was dayes light,
Up they rise, and soon hem dighte.+
Sir Ywayn and his damysel
3120   Went ful soon to a chapel,

3092 **hold** stronghold, castle.
3093 **aire** heir.
3101 **buxom and bayn** willing and eager.
3103 **Serk and breke** shirt and undergarment.
3107 **were** wear.
3118 **hem dighte** made themselves ready.

And ther they herde a messe+ in haste
That was seyde of the Holy Gaste.+
After messe ordeyned he has+
Forth on his weye faste for-to passe.
3125   At the lord his leve he taketh,
And greet thonkyng to him he maketh.
The lord seyde, "Tak it to no greve,+
To go hennes yet getest thou no leve.
Heer-inne is an unsely+ lawe
3130   That hath ben used of old dawe,+
And bus+ be don for freend or fo.
I shal do come bifore thee two
Grete sergeaunts of muchel myght;
And whether it be wrong or right,
3135   Thou moot take the sheeld and spere
Ayeines hem thee for-to were.+
If thou overcome hem in this stour,+
Than shaltow have al this honour
And my doghter in mariage,
3140   And also al myn heritage."
Than seyde Sir Ywayn, "So moot I thee,+
Thy doghter shaltow have for me;
For a kyng or an emperour
May hire wedd wyth greet honour."
3145   The lord seyde, "Heer shal come no knight
That he ne shal wyth two champiouns fighte;

3121 **messe** mass.
3122 **Gaste** = *Gost(e)*.
3123 **has** = *hath*.
3127 **greve** = *greef* grievance.
3129 **unsely** unfortunate.
3130 **of old dawe** i.e., in olden days.
3131 **bus** must necessarily.
3136 **were** defend.
3137 **stour** combat.
3141 **So moot I thee** As I hope to prosper.

So shaltow don on alle wyse,
For it is knowen custume assise."+
Sir Ywayn seyde, "Sith I shal so,
3150 Than is the beste that I may do
To putte me boldely in her hende+
And take the grace that God wyl sende."

The champiouns soon were forth broght.
Sir Ywayn seyth, "By Him me boghte,
3155 Ye seme wel the devles sones,
For I saw nevere swiche champiouns."
Either broghte unto the place
A muchel round talvace+
And a club ful greet and long
3160 Thikke fret+ wyth many a thwong;+
On bodies armed wel they were,
But her hedes bothe were bare.
The leoun bremely+ on hem bliste;+
Whan he hem saw ful wel he wiste
3165 That they sholde wyth his maister fighte;
He thoghte to helpe him at his myghte.
Wyth his tayl the erthe he dang;+
For-to fighte him thoghte ful longe.
Of him a partie+ hadde they drede;
3170 They seyde, "Sire knight, thou most nede
Do thy leoun out of this place,
For to us maketh he greet manace,
Or yelde thee to us as creaunt."+

3148 **custume assise** established custom.
3151 **hende** = *hondes.*
3158 **talvace** (wooden) shield.
3160 **fret** bound. **thwong** thong.
3163 **bremely** fiercely. **bliste** stared.
3167 **dang** struck.
3169 **a partie** somewhat.
3173 **yelde thee to us as creaunt** i.e., surrender.

He seyde, "That were noght myn avenaunt."+
3175   They seyde, "Than do thy beste aweye,
And as soon shulle we samen+ pleye."
He seyde, "Sires, if ye be agaste,
Taketh the beste and byndeth him faste."
They seyde, "He shal be bounde or slayn,
3180   For help of him shaltow have nane.+
Thy self allone shal wyth us fighte,
For that is custume and the right."
Than seyde Sir Ywayn to hem soon, ·
"Wher wol ye that the beste be don?"
3185   "In a chambre he shal be loken
Wyth gode lokkes ful stifly stoken."+
Sir Ywayn ledde than his leoun
Into a chambre to prisoun;
Than were bothe the devles ful bolde
3190   Whan the leoun was in holde.
    Sir Ywayn took his noble wede
And dighte him inne, for he hadde nede,
And on his noble stede he strod
And boldely to hem bothe he rod.
3195   His mayden was ful sore adred
That he was so streytly sted,+
And unto God faste gan she preye
For-to wynne him wel aweye.
Than strike they on him wonder sore
3200   Wyth her clubbes that ful stronge wore;+
Upon his shelde so faste they felde+

3174 **myn avenaunt** i.e., what is honorable.
3176 **samen** together.
3180 **nane** = *non.*
3186 **stifly stoken** strongly shut up.
3196 **streytly sted** sorely beset.
3200 **wore** = *were.*
3201 **felde** (?) struck with felling blows.

That nevere a pece wyth other heeld;
Wonder it is that any man
Myghte bere strokes that he took than.
3205 Mystere+ hadde he of socour,
For he cam nevere in swich a stour.
But manly evere wyth al his mayn
And graythly+ hit he hem ageyn;
And as it telleth in the book,
3210 He yaf the double of that he took.
        Ful greet sorwe the leoun has+
In the chambre wher he was;
And evere he thoghte upon that dede,
How he was helped in his nede,
3215 And he myghte now do no socour
To him that helped him in that stour:
Myghte he out of the chambre breke,
Soon he wolde his maister wreke.
He herde her strokes that were ful sterne,
3220 And yerne+ waiteth in ilke heryne—+
And al was made ful faste to holde.
Atte laste he cam to the thressh-holde:
The erthe ther caste he up ful soon,
As faste as four men sholde have don
3225 If they hadde broght bothe bille+ and spade;
A muchel hole ful soon he made.
In al this was Sir Ywayn
Ful streytly parred+ wyth muchel peyne;
And drede he hadde, as him wel oghte,
3230 For nother of hem no woundes laughte.+

3205 **Mystere** need.
3208 **graythly** promptly.
3211 **has** = *hath.*
3220 **yerne** eagerly. **in ilke heryne** i.e., in that place.
3225 **bille** pickaxe.
3228 **parred** hemmed in.
3230 **laughte** received.

Kepe⁺ hem couthe they wonder wel
That dyntes⁺ derede⁺ hem nevere a deel;
It was no wepen that man myghte welde
Myghte get a shiver⁺ out of her shelde.

3235 Ther-of couthe Ywayn no rede—⁺
Sore he douted to be dede;
And also his damysel
Ful muchel murnyng made a-melle,⁺
And wel she wende he sholde be slayn,

3240 And certes, than were hir socour gane.⁺
But faste he stightled⁺ in that stour,
And hastily him cam socour.
      Now is the leoun out-broken—
His maister shal ful soon be wroken.

3245 He renneth faste wyth ful fell rees:⁺
Than helped it noght to preye for pees;
He stirte unto that oon glotoun⁺
And to the erthe he breyde⁺ him doun.
Than was ther non aboute that place

3250 That they ne were fayne of that faire chace
(The mayden hadde greet joye in herte);
They seyde, "He shal nevere rise in querte."⁺
His felawe fraisted⁺ wyth al his mayn
To raise him smertly up ageyn;

3231 **Kepe** protect.
3232 **dyntes** strokes, blows. **derede** harmed.
3234 **shiver** bit, splinter.
3235 **couthe . . . no rede** i.e., knew of nothing to do about it.
3238 **a-melle** i.e., meantime.
3240 **gane** = *gon.*
3241 **stightled** contended.
3245 **rees** rush, haste.
3247 **glotoun** vile fellow.
3248 **breyde** pulled.
3252 **querte** health, sound condition.
3253 **fraisted** tried.

3255   And right so as he stouped doun,
Sir Ywayn wyth his brond⁺ was boun,⁺
And strok his nek-bon right asonder:
Ther-of the folk hadde muchel wonder.
His heved⁺ trindled⁺ on the sond;
3260   Thus hadde Ywayn the heigher hond.
Whan he hadde feld that foule feloun,
Of his stede he lighted doun.
His leoun on that other lay;
Now wyl he helpe him, if he may.
3265   The leoun saw his maister come,
And to his partie he wolde have som.
The righte shulder awey he raketh,
Bothe arm and club wyth him he taketh,
And so his maister gan he wreke.
3270   And as he myghte, yet gan he speke
And seyde, "Sire knight, for thy gentry,
I preye thee have of me mercy;
And by skile⁺ shal he mercy have,
What man so mekely wyl it crave;
3275   And ther-fore graunt mercy to me."
Sir Ywayn seyde, "I graunte it thee
If that thou wylt thy selven seye
That thou are overcome this day."
He seyde, "I graunte, wythout faile,
3280   I am overcomen in this bataile
For pure atteynt and recreaunt."⁺
Sir Ywayn seyde, "Now I thee graunte
For-to do thee no more dere,⁺

3256 **brond** sword. **boun** ready.
3259 **heved** = *heed*. **trindled** trundled, rolled.
3273 **by skile** as is reasonable.
3281 **atteynt and recreaunt** exhaustion and defeat.
3283 **dere** injury.

And from my leoun I shal thee were: +
3285   I graunte thee pees at my powere."

Than come the folk ful faire y-fere.
The lord and the lady als
They toke him faire aboute the hals; +
They seyde, "Sire now shaltow be
3290   Lord and sire in this contree,
And wedde oure doghter, for certeyn."
Sir Ywayn answerde than ageyn;
He seyde, "Sith ye yeve me hire now,
I yeve hire evene ageyn to you;
3295   Of me for evere I graunte hire quite. +
But, Sire, taketh it to no despite,
For, certes, wyf may I non wedde
Until my nedes be bettre sped.
But this thyng, Sire, I axe of thee,
3300   That alle thise prisouns may passe free.
God hath graunted me this chaunce,
I have made her deliveraunce."
The lord answerde than ful tite
And seyde, "I graunte thee hem al quite.
3305   My doghter als I rede thou take:
She is noght worthy to forsake."
Unto the knight Sir Ywayn seys, +
"Sire, I shal noght hire myspreyse;
For she is so curteis and hende
3310   That from hennes to the worldes ende
Is no kyng ne emperour
Ne no man of so greet honour

3284 **were** protect.
3288 **hals** neck.
3295 **quite** to be free.
3307 **seys** = *seyth*.

That he ne myghte wedde that burde+ brighte;
And so wolde I, if that I myghte.
3315 I wolde hire wedde wyth ful good chere,
But, lo, I have a mayden here;
To folwe hire now moot I nede
Whider-so she wyl me lede.
Ther-fore at this tyme haveth good-day."
3320 He seyde, "Thou passest noght so awey.
Sith thou wylt noght do as I telle,
In my prisoun shaltow dwelle."
He seyde, "If I laye ther al my lyf,
I shal hire nevere wedde to wyf;
3325 For wyth this mayden moot I wende
Until we come wher she wyl lende."+
The lord saw it was no boot+
Aboute that matere more to mote.+
He yaf him leve awey to fare,
3330 But he hadde levere he hadde ben thare.+
  Sir Ywayn taketh than forth y-fere
Alle the prisouns that ther were;
Bifore him soon they come echoon,
Nere-hond naked and wo-bigon.
3335 Stille he hoved+ at the yate
Til they were went al forth ther-at.
Two and two ay wente they samen,
And made among hem muchel gamen;
If God hadde come from hevene on hight
3340 And on this molde+ among hem light,

3313 **burde** young woman.
3326 **lende** remain.
3327 **no boot** to no avail.
3328 **mote** argue.
3330 **thare** = *ther*.
3335 **hoved** waited.
3340 **molde** earth.

They hadde noght made more joye, certeyn,
Thanne they made to Sir Ywayn.
Folk of the toun come him biforn
And blessede the tyme that he was born;
3345 Of his prowesse were they wel payde:+
"In this world is non swich," they seyde.
They conveyde him out of the toun
Wyth a faire processioun.
The maydens than her leve have tane,
3350 Ful muchel myrthe they made ilkane;+
At her departyng preyde they thus:
"Oure lord God, myghty Jhesus,
He helpe you, Sire, to have youre wyl
And shilde you evere from al-kyn il."
3355 "Maydens," he seyde, "God mote you see,+
And brynge you wel wher ye wolde be."
Thus her weye forther they wente:
No more unto hem wol we tente.+

Sir Ywayn and his faire may
3360 Al the seven-nyght travailde they.
The mayden knew the weye ful wel
Home unto that ilke castel
Wher she lefte the sike may;
And thider hastily come they.
3365 Whan they come to the castel yate,
She ledde Sir Ywayn in ther-at.
The mayden was yet sike lyinge,
But whan they tolde hire this tidynge
That comen was hir messager,
3370 And the knight wyth hire y-fere,

3345 **payde** pleased.
3350 **ilkane** = *echoon.*
3355 **God mote you see** may God look with favor on you.
3358 **tente** take notice.

Swich joye ther-of she hadde in herte,
Hire thoghte that she were al in querte.
She seyde, "I wot my suster wyl
Yeve me now that falleth me til."+

3375 In hir herte she was so light,
Ful hendely haylsed+ she the knight:
"A, Sire," she seyde, "God do thee mede
That thou wolde come in swich a nede."
And all that in that castel were

3380 Welcomde him wyth myrie chere.
I can noght seye, so God me gladde,
Half the myrthe that they him made.
That nyght he hadde ful noble reste
Wyth al-kyn esement of the beste.

3385 As soon as the day was sent,
They ordeynde hem+ and forth they went.

Unto that toun faste gonne they ride
Wher the kyng sojourned that tide;
And ther the elder suster lay

3390 Redy for-to kepe hir day.
She trusted wel on Sir Gawayn
That no knight sholde come him ageyn;
She hoped ther was no knight lyvande+
In bataile that myghte wyth him stande.+

3395 Al a seven-nyght dayes bidene
Wolde noght Sir Gawayn be sene,
But in an other toun he lay;
For he wolde come at the day

3374 **til** = *to*.
3376 **haylsed** greeted.
3386 **ordeynde hem** made themselves ready.
3393 **lyvande** = *lyvynge*.
3394 **stande** = *stonde*.

As aunturous[+] into the place

3400 So that no man sholde see his face;
The armes he bar were noght his owene,
For he wolde noght in court be knowen.

Sir Ywayn and his damysel
Into the toun toke her hostel;

3405 And ther he heeld him prively
So that non sholde him ascrie.[+]
Hadde they dwelt lenger by a day,
Than hadde she lorn hir lond for ay.
Sir Ywayn rested ther that nyght,

3410 And on the morne he gan him dighte;
On slepe lefte they his leoun,
And wonne[+] hem wightly out of toun.
It was hir wyl, and als his owene,
To come to court as knight unknowen.

3415 Soon aboute the pryme of day,
Sir Gawayn from thennes ther[+] he lay
Hyeth him faste into the felde
Wel armed wyth spere and shelde;
No man knew him, lasse ne more,

3420 But she that he sholde fighte for.
The elder suster to court com[+]
Unto the kyng to axe hir doom;[+]
She seyde, "I am come wyth my knight
Al redy to defende my right.

3425 This day was us set sesoun,[+]

3399 **aunturous** i.e., one seeking adventures.
3406 **ascrie** inform upon.
3412 **wonne** got, went.
3416 **ther** (there) where.
3421 **com** = *cam*.
3422 **doom** decision, judgment.
3425 **us set sesoun** set for us as the appointed time.

And I am heer al redy boun;
And sith this is the laste day,
Yeveth doom and letteth us wende oure way.
My suster hath alle sides soght,
3430 But, wel I wot, heer cometh she noght;
For, certeynly, she fyndeth nane +
That dar the bataile undertane
This day for hire for-to fighte
For-to reve from me my right.
3435 Now have I wel wonne my lond
Wythouten dynt of knightes hond.
What so my suster evere hath mynt, +
Al hir partie now telle I tynt; +
Al is myn to selle and yive: +
3440 As a wrecche ay shal she lyve.
Ther-fore, Sire Kyng, sith it is so,
Yeveth youre doom and lat us go."
The kyng seyde, "Mayden, thenk noght longe."
(Wel he wiste she hadde the wrong.)
3445 "Damysel, it is the assise, +
Whil sittyng is of the justice,
The doom nedes thou most abide;
For par aventure it may bitide
Thy suster shal come al by-tyme, +
3450 For it is litel passed pryme." +
Whan the kyng hadde told his skile, +
They sawe come ridynge over a hil
The yonger suster and hir knight:

3431 **nane** = *non.*
3437 **mynt** attempted.
3438 **telle I tynt** I count (as) lost.
3439 **yive** = *yeve* give.
3445 **assise** custom.
3449 **by-tyme** in (good) time.
3450 **pryme** midmorning.
3451 **skile** reason.

The weye to toun they toke ful right.
3455 On Ywayns bed his leoun lay,
And they hadde stolen from him awey.
The elder mayden made il chere
Whan they to court comen were.
The kyng wythdrough his juggement,
3460 For wel he trowed in his entente+
That the yonger suster hadde the right,
And that she sholde come wyth som knight;
Himself knew hire wel ynough.
Whan he hire saw, ful faste he lough:+
3465 Him liked it wel in his herte
That he saw hire so in querte.
    Into the court she took the weye,
And to the kyng thus gan she seye,
"God that governeth al-kyn thyng
3470 Thee save and see, Sire Arthur the Kyng,
And alle the knights that longeth to thee,
And also al thy myrie meynee.
Unto youre court, Sire, have I broght
An uncouth+ knight that ye knowe noght;
3475 He seyth that soothly for my sake
This bataile wyl he undertake;
And he hath yet in other londe
Ful felle dedes under honde;
But al he leveth, God do him mede,
3480 For-to helpe me in my nede."
Hir elder suster stood hire by
And to hire seyde she hastily,
"For His love that leneth us lyf,
Yif me my right wythouten strif,
3485 And lat no men ther-fore be slayn."

3460 **entente** mind.
3464 **lough** laughed.
3474 **uncouth** strange, foreign.

The elder suster seyde ageyn:
"Thy right is noght, for al is myne,
And I wyl have it maugree+ thyne.
Ther-fore if thou preche al day,
3490 Heer shaltow no-thyng bere awey."
The yonger mayden to hir seys:+
"Suster, thou art ful curteis,
And greet dol is it for-to see
Swiche two knightes as they be
3495 For us shulle putte hemself to spille.+
Ther-fore now, if it by thy wylle,
Of thy good wylt thou me give+
Somthyng that I may on lyve."
    The elder suster seyde, "So moot I thee,
3500 Whoso is feerd, I rede they flee.
Thou getest right noght, wythouten faile,
But if thou wynne it thurgh bataile."
The yonger seyde, "Sith thou wylt swa,+
To the grace of God heer I me ta;+
3505 And Lord as He is moste of myght,
He sende his socour to that knight
That thus in dede of charitee
This day auntres+ his lyf for me."

    The two knightes come bifore the kyng;
3510 And ther was soon ful greet gadryng,+
For ilke man that walke myghte
Hasted soon to see that sight.

3488 **maugree** in spite of.
3491 **seys** = *seyth.*
3495 **spille** destroy.
3497 **give** = *yeve.*
3503 **swa** = *so.*
3504 **ta** betake (myself).
3508 **auntres** ventures, hazards.
3510 **gadryng** gathering.

Of hem this was a sely + cas,
That nother wiste what other was;
3515   Ful greet love was bitwixe hem two,
And now ben either othres fo;
Ne the kyng couthe hem noght knowe,
For they wolde noght her faces shewe.
If either of hem hadde other sene,
3520   Greet love hadde ben hem bitwene;
Now was this a greet sely +
That trewe love and so greet envy
As bitwixe hem two was than
Myghte bothe at ones be in a man.
3525   The knightes for tho maydens love
Either to other caste a glove,
And wel armed wyth spere and shelde
They riden bothe forth to the felde;
They strike her stedes that were kene;
3530   Litel love was hem bitwene.
Ful grevously bigan that gamen:
Wyth stalworth speres strike they samen; +
And they hadde ones togidre spoken,
Hadde ther ben no speres broken;
3535   But in that tyme bitid + it so
That either of hem wolde other slo. +
They drowe swerdes and swonge aboute—
To dele dyntes hadde they no doute. +
Her sheldes were shivrede and helmes riven: +
3540   Ful stalworth strokes were than yeven.

3513 **sely** strange, wondrous.
3521 **sely** wonder, marvel.
3532 **samen** together.
3535 **bitid** happened, befell.
3536 **slo** =*slee*.
3538 **doute** fear (of danger).
3539 **riven** split.

Bothe on bak and brestes thore+
Were bothe wounded wonder sore;
In many stedes myghte men kenne+
The blood out of her bodies renne.
3545 On helmes they yave swiche strokes kene
That the riche stones al bidene
And other gere that was ful good
Was over-covered al in blood.
Her helmes were yvele brosten+ bothe,
3550 And they also were wonder wrothe.
Her hauberkes+ als were al to-torn
Bothe bihynde and als biforn;
Her sheldes laye shivred on the grounde.
They restede than a litel stounde
3555 For-to take her ande+ hem til—+
And that was wyth her bother+ wyl.
But ful longe restede they noght
Til either of hem of other soghte;
A strenger stour was hem bitwene,
3560 Harder hadde men nevere sene.
    The kyng and other that ther were
Seyde that they sawe nevere er
So noble knightes in no place
So longe fighte but by Goddes grace.
3565 Barouns, knightes, squiers, and knaves
Seyde, "It is no man that haves+
So muchel tresour ne nobleye+

3541 **thore** = *ther.*
3543 **kenne** perceive.
3549 **brosten** burst.
3551 **hauberkes** (coats of) chain mail.
3555 **ande** breath. **til** = *to.*
3556 **her bother** of both of them.
3559 *strenger* for MS. *stronge.*
3566 **haves** = *hath.*
3567 **nobleye** nobility.

That myghte hem quite+ her dede this day."
Thise wordes herde the knightes two:
3570   It made hem for-to be more thro.+
    Knightes wente aboute gode wone+
To make the two susters at one;
But the elder was so unkynde,
In hire they myghte no mercy fynde;
3575   And the right that the yonger hase,+
Putteth she in the kynges grace.
The kyng himself and als the quene
And other knightes al bidene
And alle that sawe that dede that day
3580   Helde al wyth the yonger may;
And to the kyng all they bisoghte,
Whether the elder wolde or noght,
That he sholde evene the londes dele
And yeve the yonger damysel
3585   The half or elles som porcioun,+
That she may have to warisoun,+
And parte the two knightes in-twynne.+
"For certes," they seyde, "it were greet synne
That either of hem sholde other slo,+
3590   For in the world is noght swiche two.
Whan othre knightes," seyde they, "sholde cesse,+
Hemself wolde noght assente to pese."+
Alle that evere sawe that bataile

3568 **quite** requite.
3570 **thro** stubborn, determined not to give way.
3571 **gode wone** in great numbers.
3575 **hase** = *hath.*
3585 **porcioun** portion.
3586 **warisoun** reward, wealth.
3587 **in-twynne** in two.
3589 **slo** = *slee.*
3591 **cesse** cease.
3592 **pese** (grant?) peace, (?) appease.

Of her myght hadde greet merveil;
3595 They sawe nevere under the hevene
Two knightes that were couplede+ so evene.
Of al the folk was non so wys
That wiste whether+ sholde have the pris;
For they sawe nevere so stalworth stour:
3600 Ful dere boghte they that honour.

Greet wonder hadde Sir Gawayn
What he was that faught him ageyn;
And Sir Ywayn hadde greet ferly+
Who stood ayeins him so stifly.
3605 On this wyse lasted that fight
From mid-morne unto myrke+ nyght;
And by that tyme, I trowe, they two
Were ful wery and sore also.
They hadde bled so muchel blood,
3610 It was greet ferly+ that they stode,
So sore they bete on bak and brest
Until the sonne was gon to reste;
For nother of hem wolde other spare.
For myrke+ myghte they than no mare;+
3615 Ther-fore to reste they bothe hem yelde.
But er they passede out of the felde,
Bitwixe hem two myghte men see
Bothe muchel joye and greet pitee.
By speche myghte no man Gawayn knowe,
3620 So was he hors+ and spak ful lowe;

3596 **couplede** matched.
3598 **whether** which (of the two).
3603 **ferly** wonder.
3606 **myrke** dark.
3610 **ferly** wonder.
3614 **myrke** darkness. **mare** = *more*.
3620 **hors** hoarse.

And muchel was he out of maught+
For the strokes that he hadde laught;+
And Sir Ywayn was ful wery,
But thus he speketh and seyth in hye;
3625 He seyde, "Sire, sith us fayleth light,
I hope it be no lyvynge wight
That wyl us blame if that we twynne.+
For of alle stedes I have ben inne,
Wyth no man yet nevere I mette
3630 That so wel couthe his strokes sette;
So noble strokes hast thou yeven
That my sheeld is al to-riven."
    Sir Gawayn seyde, "Sire, certeynly,
Thou are noght so wery as I;
3635 For if we lenger fightynge were,
I trowe I myghte do thee no dere.
Thou are no-thyng in my dette
Of strokes that I on thee sette."
Sir Ywayn seyde, "In Cristes name,
3640 Sey me what thou hot+ at hame."+
He seyde, "Sith thou my name wylt here
And coveytest+ to wite what it were,
My name in this londe many wote:+
I hote Gawayn, the kyng sone Lot."+
3645 Than was Sir Ywayn sore agast;
His swerd from him he caste.
He feerd right as he wolde wede,+
And soon he stirte doun of his stede.

3621 **maught** = *myght.*
3622 **laught** received.
3627 **twynne** part.
3640 **hot** are called. **hame** = *hom(e).*
3642 **coveytest** desire.
3643 **wote** = *wite.*
3644 **the kyng sone Lot** King Lot's son.
3647 **wede** became mad.

He seyde, "Heer is a foule myschaunce
3650   For defaute of conisaunce.+
A, Sire," he seyde, "hadde I thee seen,
Than hadde heer no bataile ben;
I hadde me yolden to thee as tite,
As worthy were for disconfit."
3655   "What man artow?" seyde Sir Gawayn.
"Sire," he seyde, "I hote Ywayn,
That loveth thee more by see and sande+
Thanne any man that is lyvande,+
For many dedes that thou me dide
3660   And curteisye ye have me kidd.+
Ther-fore, Sire, now in this stour
I shal do thee this honour:
I graunte that thou hast me overcomen
And by strengthe in bataile nomen."+
3665   Sir Gawayn answerde as curteis:
"Thou shalt noght do, Sire, as thou seys;+
This honour shal noght be myne,
But, certes, it oweth wel to be thyne.
I yeve it thee heer wythouten hone+
3670   And graunte that I am undon."
Soon they lighte, so seyth the book,
And either other in armes toke
And kiste so ful fele sithe;+
Than were they bothe glade and blithe.

3675   In armes so they stode togidre

3650 **defaute of conisaunce** lack of understanding, recognition.
3657 **by see and sande** i.e., everywhere, always.
3658 **lyvande** = *lyvynge.*
3660 **kidd** shown.
3664 **nomen** taken.
3666 **seys** = *seyst.*
3669 **hone** delay.
3673 **fele sithe** many times.

Until the kyng cam ridynge thider;
And faste he coveyt⁺ for-to here
Of thise knightes what they were,
And why they made so muchel gamen,
3680 Sith they hadde so foghten samen.
Ful hendely than axed the kyng
Who hadde so soon made saghtelyng⁺
Bitwixe hem that hadde ben so wrathe⁺
And either hadde don other scathe.⁺
3685 He seyde, "I wende ye wolde ful fayn
Either of you have other slayn,
And now ye ben so⁺ frendes dere."
"Sire Kyng," seyde Gawayn, "Ye shulle here.
For unknowyng and harde grace
3690 Thus have we foghten in this place.
I am Gawayn, youre owene nevow,⁺
And Sir Ywayn faught wyth me now.
Whan we were nere wery, y-wis,
My name he frayned⁺ and I his;
3695 Whan we were knowen, soon gan we cesse.
But, certes, Sire, this is no lees,⁺
Hadde we foghten forth a stounde,
I wot wel I hadde gon to grounde;
By his prowesse and his mayn,
3700 I wot, for sothe, I hadde ben slayn."
    Thise wordes mengede⁺ al the mood⁺
Of Sir Ywayn as he stood;

3677 **coveyt** desired.
3682 **saghtelyng** peace.
3683 **wrathe** = *wroth(e)* angry.
3684 **scathe** injury.
3687 **so** as.
3691 **nevow** nephew.
3694 **frayned** inquired, asked.
3696 **lees** falsehood.
3701 **mengede** disturbed. **mood** heart.

"Sire," he seyde, "so moot I go,
Ye knowe youre self it is noght so.

3705 Sire Kyng," he seyde, "wythouten faile,
I am overcomen in this bataile."
"Nay, certes," seyde Gawayn, "but am I."
Thus nother wolde have the maistrye;
Bifore the kyng gan either graunte

3710 That himself was recreaunt.+
Than the kyng and his meynee
Hadde bothe joye and greet pitee;
He was ful fayn they frendes were,
And that they were so founden y-fere.

3715 The kyng seyde, "Now is wel sene
That muchel love was you bitwene."
He seyde, "Sir Ywayn, welcome hom!"
For it was longe sith he ther com.+
He seyde, "I rede ye bothe assente

3720 To do you in my juggement,
And I shal make so good an ende
That ye shulle bothe be holden hende."+
They bothe assented soon ther-til,+
To don hem in the kynges wyl,

3725 If the maydens wolde do so.
Than the kyng bad knightes two
Wende after the maydens bathe;+
And so they dide ful swithe rathe.+

Bifore the kyng whan they were broght,
3730 He tolde unto hem as him thoghte:

3710 **recreaunt** conceding defeat.
3718 **com** = *cam.*
3722 **holden hende** held (to be) courteous.
3723 **ther-til** = *ther-to.*
3727 **bathe** = *bothe.*
3728 **rathe** quickly.

"Listeneth me, now, maydens hende,
Youre greet debat is broght to ende.
So fer forth now is it driven
That the doom moot nedes be yeven,
3735   And I shal deme you as I can."
The elder suster answerde than,
"Sith ye ben kyng than us sholde were,+
I preye you do to me no dere."+
He seyde, "I wyl lete for no sawe+
3740   For-to do the londes lawe.
Thy yonge suster shal have hir right,
For I see wel that thy knight
Is overcomen in this were."+
Thus seyde he only hire to fere+
3745   And for he wiste hir wyl ful wel,
That she wolde parte wyth nevere a deel.+
"Sire," she seyde, "sith thus is gon,
Now moot I, whether I wyl or non,
Al youre comaundement fulfille;
3750   And ther-fore do right as ye wylle."+
The kyng seyde, "Thus shal it falle:
Alle youre londes departe I shal.
Thy wyl is wrong, that have I knowen;
Now shaltow have noght but thyn owene,
3755   That is half of al bidene."
Than answerde she ful tite in tene+
And seyde, "Me think'th ful greet outrage
To yeve hire half myn heritage."

3737 **were** protect.
3738 **dere** injury, harm.
3739 **sawe** saying.
3743 **were** trouble, hostility.
3744 **fere** frighten.
3746 **nevere a deel** no portion (of it).
3750 **wylle** = *wol* wish.
3756 **tene** anger.

The kyng seyde, "For youre bother⁺ ese,

3760   In hir lond I shal hir sese,⁺

And she shal holde hir lond of thee

And to thee ther-fore make feautee;⁺

She shal thee love as hir lady,

And thou shalt kithe⁺ thy curteisye,

3765   Love hire after thyn avenaunt,⁺

And she shal be to thee tenaunt."

This lond was first, I understonde,

That evere was parted in Englelonde.

Than seyde the kyng, wythouten faile,

3770   For the love of that bataile,

Alle susters that sholde after ben

Sholde parte the londes hem bitwene.

Than seyde the kyng to Sir Gawayn,

And als he preyde Sir Ywayn,

3775   For-to unlace her riche wede;

And ther-to hadde they greet nede.

As they thusgate⁺ stode and speke,

The leoun out of the chambre breke;⁺

As they her armures sholde unlace,

3780   Cam he rennynge to that place.

But he hadde, er he cam ther,

Soght his maister whider-wher;⁺

And ful muchel joye he made

Whan he his maister founden hadde.

3785   On ilke side than myghte men see

3759 **youre bother** of both of you.
3760 **sese** put in legal possession.
3762 **feautee** fealty.
3764 **kithe** show.
3765 **thyn avenaunt** i.e., what is honorable.
3777 **thusgate** in this manner.
3778 **breke** =*brak* broke.
3782 **whider-wher** far and wide.

The folk faste to toun gan flee;
So were they ferde for the leoun
Whan they sawe him thider boun.
Sir Ywayn bad hem come ageyn
3790 And seyde, "Lordynges, for certeyn,
From this beste I shal you were⁺
So that he shal you do no dere;
And, Sires, ye shulle wel trowe my sawes:⁺
We ben frendes and gode felawes.
3795 He is myne and I am his:
For no tresour I wolde him mysse."⁺
   Whan they sawe this was certeyn,
Than speke they alle of Sir Ywayn:
"This is the knight wyth the leoun
3800 That is holden of so greet renoun.
This ilke knight the geaunt slough—
Of dedes he is doughty ynough."
Than seyde Sir Gawayn soon in hye,
"Me is bitidd greet vilanye;
3805 I crie thee mercy, Sir Ywayn,
That I have trespast thee ageyn.
Thou helped my suster in hir nede;
Yvele have I quit⁺ thee now thy mede.
Thou auntured⁺ thy lyf for love of me;
3810 And as my suster tolde of thee,
Thou seyde that we ful fele dawes⁺
Hadde ben frendes and gode felawes.
But who it was ne wiste I noght.
Sithen have I had ful muchel thoght,

3791 **were** protect.
3793 **sawes** sayings, i.e., words.
3796 **mysse** do without.
3808 **quit** requited.
3809 **auntured** ventured, risked.
3811 **dawes** = *dayes*.

3815   And yet for al that I do can,
      I couthe nevere here of no man
      That me couthe telle in tour ne toun
      Of the knight wyth the leoun."
        Whan they hadde unlaced her wede,
3820   Alle the folk toke ful good hede
      How that beste his bales to bete⁺
      Likked his maister bothe hondes and feet.
      Alle the men greet merveil hadde
      Of the myrthe the leoun made.
3825   Whan the knightes were broght to reste,
      The kyng gert⁺ come soon of the beste
      Surgiens that evere were sene
      For-to helpe hem bothe bidene.

        Soon as they were hole and sounde,
3830   Sir Ywayn hyeth⁺ him faste to founde.
      Love was so in his herte fest,⁺
      Nyght ne day hadde he no reste;
      But he gete grace of his lady,
      He moot go wood or for love dy.⁺
3835   Ful prively forth gan he wende
      Out of the court from ilke frende.
      He rideth right unto the welle,
      And ther he thenketh for-to dwelle.
      His good leoun went wyth him ay,
3840   He wolde noght parte from him awey.
      He caste water upon the ston:
      The storm ros ful soon anon,

3821 **his bales to bete** to assuage his misfortunes.
3826 **gert** caused (to).
3830 **hyeth** set out (to travel).
3831 **fest** held, fastened.
3834 **dy** = *deye* die.

The thonder grisly+ gan outbreste:
Him thoghte as al the grete forest
3845 And al that was aboute the welle
Sholde have sonken into helle.
    The lady was in muchel doute,
For alle the castel walles aboute
Quoke so faste than men myghte thinke+
3850 That al into the erthe sholde synke;
They tremblede faste, bothe bour and halle,
As they unto the grounde sholde falle.
Was nevere in this myddel-erde+
In no castel folk so ferde.+
3855 But who it was wiste wel Lunete;
She seyde, "Now ben we harde bisete;
Madame, I ne wot what us is beste,
For heer now mowe we have no reste.
Ful wel I wot ye have no knight
3860 That dar wende to youre welle and fighte
Wyth him that cometh you to assaile;
And if he have heer no bataile,
Ne fynde non you to defende,
Youre los+ beth lorn wythouten ende."
3865 The lady seyde she wolde be dede;
"Dere Lunete, what is thy rede?
Werke I wyl by thy counseil,
For I ne wot noght what may avayle."
"Madame," she seyde, "I wolde ful fayn
3870 Counseile you if it myght gayne.
But in this cas it were mystere+

3843 grisly terribly, awfully.
3849 thinke = *thenke.*
3853 myddel-erde middle-earth, i.e., world.
3854 ferde frightened.
3864 los fame, renown.
3871 mystere (a) necessity.

To have a wyser counseiler."
And by deceit than gan she seye,
"Madame, par chaunce this ilke day
3875   Some of youre knightes mowe come hame+
And you defende of al this shame."
"A," she seyde, "Lunete, lat be;
Speek no more of my meynee;
For wel I wot, so God me mende,
3880   I have no knight me may defende.
Ther-fore my counseil bus+ thee be,
And I wyl werke al+ after thee,
And ther-fore help at al thy myght."
"Madame," she seyde, "hadde we that knight
3885   That is so curteis and avenaunt+
And hath slayn the grete geaunt,
And als that the three knightes slough,
Of him ye myghte be triste+ ynough.
But forther-more, Madame, I wot
3890   He and his lady ben at debat,
And have ben so ful many day;
And as I herde him selven seye,
He wolde bileve wyth no lady
But on this covenaunt utterly,
3895   That they wolde make certeyn oth
To do her myght and connyng+ bothe
Trewely bothe by day and naght+
To make him and his lady saght."+

3875 **hame** = *hom(e)*.
3881 **bus** it behooves.
3882 **al** i.e., your counsel.
3885 **avenaunt** honorable.
3888 **triste** trusty, trusting.
3896 **connyng** wit, intelligence.
3897 **naght** = *nyght*.
3898 **saght** in agreement.

The lady answerde soon hire til,+
3900 "That wyl I do wyth ful good wyl;
Unto thee heer my trouthe I plighte
That I shal ther-to do my myght."
She seyde, "Madame, be ye noght wroth,
I moot nedes have of you an oth
3905 So that I may be certeyn."
The lady seyde, "That wyl I fayn."+
Lunete than riche relikes took,
The chalice and the messe-book;
On knees the lady doun hire sette
3910 (Wite ye wel, than liked Lunete),
Hir hond upon the book she leyde,
And Lunete al-thus to hire seyde,
"Madame," she seyde, "thou shalt swere heer
That thou shalt do thy power
3915 Bothe day and nyghte upon al wyse
Wythouten any-kyn feyntise+
To saghtel+ the knight wyth the leoun
And his lady of greet renoun,
So that no faute+ be founden in thee."
3920 She seyde, "I graunte, it shal so be."
Than was Lunete wel payed of this;
The book she gert+ hir lady kisse.

Soon a palfrey she bistrod,
And on hir weye faste forth she rod;
3925 The nexte weye ful soon she nam,+

3899 **til** = _to_.
3906 **wyl I fayn** will I (do) gladly.
3916 **feyntise** guile, deceit.
3917 **saghtel** come to agreement (with).
3919 **faute** fault.
3922 **gert** caused.
3925 **nam** took.

Until she to the welle cam.
Sir Ywayn sat under the thorn,
And his leoun lay him biforn.
She knew him wel by his leoun,
3930 And hastily she lighted doun;
And as soon as he Lunete saugh,+
In his herte than list him laughe.+
Muchel myrthe was whan they mette—
Either other ful faire hath gret.+
3935 She seyde, "I love greet God in trone
That I have you founde so soon,
And tidynges telle I you biforn;
Other shal my lady be manesworn+
On relikes and by bokes brade,+
3940 Or elles ye two ben frendes made."
Sir Ywayn than was wonder glad
For the tidynges that he hadde;
He thonked hir ful fele sithe
That she wolde him swich goodnesse kithe;+
3945 And she him thonked muchel mare+
For the dedes that were don are.+
So either was in othres dette,
That bothe her travail was wel set.
He seyth, "Toldest thou hire oght my name?"
3950 She seyde, "Nay, than were I to blame;
Thy name she shal noght wite for me
Til ye have kiste and saghtled be."

Than ride they forth toward the toun,

3931 saugh = saw.
3932 list him laughe he desired to laugh.
3934 gret greeted.
3938 manesworn forsworn.
3939 brade = brode broad.
3944 kithe show.
3945 mare = more.
3946 are = er before.

And wyth hem ran the gode leoun.
3955 Whan they come to the castel yate,
Al wente they in ther-at.
They speke no word to no man born
Of alle the folk they founde biforn.
As soon as the lady herde seyn
3960 Hir damysel was comen ageyn,
And als the leoun and the knight,
Than in hir herte she was ful light;
She coveyt+ evere of alle thyng
Of him to have knowelechyng.+
3965 Sir Ywayn soon on knees him sette
Whan he wyth the lady mette.
Lunete seyde to the lady soon,
"Taketh up the knight, Madame, have don!
And, as covenaunt bitwixe us was,
3970 Maketh his pees faste er he passe."
Than dide the lady him up rise;
"Sire," she seyde, "upon alle wyse
I wyl me peyne+ in alle thyng
For-to make thy saghtelyng+
3975 Bitwixe thee and thy lady bright."
"Madame," seyde Lunete, "that is right,
For non but ye hath that power.
Al the sooth now shulle ye here."
"Madame," she seyde, "is noght to layne,+
3980 This is my lord Sir Ywayn.
Swich love God bitwixe you sende
That may laste to youre lyves ende."
Than went the lady fer a-bak,

3963 **coveyt** desired.
3964 **knowelechyng** knowledge, acquaintance.
3973 **I wyl me peyne** I will take pains.
3974 **saghtelyng** reconciliation.
3979 **layne** to be hidden.

And longe she stood er that she spak.
3985 She seyde, "How is this, damysel?
I wende thou sholde be to me lele,+
That makest me, whether I wyl or noght,
Love hem that me wo have wroght;
So that me bus+ be forsworn
3990 Or love hem that wolde I were lorn.
But, whether it turne to wel or il,
That I have seyde, I shal fulfille."
Wite ye wel, than Sir Ywayn
Of tho wordes was ful fayn.
3995 "Madame," he seyde, "I have myswroght,
And that I have ful dere boght.
Greet folye I dide, the sooth to seye,
Whan that I passed my terme-day;
And certes, whoso hadde so bitidd
4000 They sholde have don right as I dide.
But I shal nevere thurgh Goddes grace
At my myght do more trespas;
And what man so wyl mercy crave,
By Goddes lawe he shal it have."
4005 Than she assented saghtelyng to make;
And soon in armes he gan hire take
And kiste hire ful ofte sithe:
Was he nevere er so blithe.

Now hath Sir Ywayn endyng made
4010 Of alle the sorwes that he hadde.
Ful lely+ loved he evere his wyf
And she him as hir owene lyf:
That lasted to her lyves ende.
And trewe Lunete, the mayden hende,

3986 **lele** loyal, faithful.
3989 **me bus** (it) behooves me.
4011 **lely** faithfully.

4015 Was honoured evere wyth olde and yinge+
And lyved at hir owene likyng;
Of al-kyn thyng she hath maistrye
Next the lord and the lady;
Alle honourde hire in tour and toun.
4020 Thus the knight wyth the leoun
Is turned now to Sir Ywayn
And hath his lordshipe al ageyn;
And so Sir Ywayn and his wyf
In joye and blisse they ladde her lyf.
4025 So dide Lunete and the leoun
Until that deeth hath driven hem doun.

Of hem no more have I herd telle,
Nother in romaunce ne in spelle.+
But Jhesu Crist for His grete grace
4030 In hevene-blisse graunte us a place
To bide inne, if His wylle be.
Amen, amen, par charitee.

4015 **yinge** = *yonge.*
4028 **spelle** tale, talk.

Glossary

This is a selective glossary to supplement the footnote glossing of the texts. It lists words that occur repeatedly, brings together inflectionally related forms, distinguishes forms that may sometimes be confused, and gives equivalents of common contractions. Forms of pronouns are listed in the Introduction, p. xxviii.

Inflectional forms of nouns, adjectives, and verbs are given only when they may not be recognizable from Modern English cognates. Unlabeled principal parts of verbs are to be understood as preterit singular and past participle if two forms appear in parentheses following the headword, and as preterit singular, preterit plural, and past participle if three forms appear.

abeye(n) to pay for, requite

adrede(n) (**adradde, adred**) to fear, be afraid

ageyn again, back, in return, in response; against; opposite

al (*adj. and pronominal*) *pl.* **alle** all, every; everything

al (*adv.*) entirely, very, quite, wholly

al-kyn every kind (of)

als, also, (*adv.*) also, equally, similarly; as; (*conj.*) as, as if

    als(o) soon as soon as

amende(n) to make better, improve, make amends, set right

and and; if

anon at once, forthwith, straightway

    anon right immediately, at once; directly

armure armor

artow = art thou

atte = at the

aventure, aunture chance; venture, feat, notable occurrence

    par aventure by chance

    in aventure in case, on the chance that

axe(n) to ask, inquire; require

ay always, ever, continually, on every occasion

ayein(e)s against; toward

bad *see* **bidde(n)**

bale torment, misery, misfortune, sorrow

band *see* **bynde(n)**

bar *see* **bere(n)**

be(n) (*Pres. s.* 1 **am,** 2 **art, best,** 3 **is, beth;** *pl.* **ben;** *pres. subj. s.* **be,** *pl.* **ben.** *Pret. s.* 1, 3 **was.** 2 **were;** *pl.* **weren;** *pret. subj. s.* **were,** *pl.* **weren.** *P.P.* **ben, i-be.** *Imp. s.* **be,** *pl.* **beth**) to be

bere(n) (**bar, beren, born / bore**) to bear, carry; give birth to; possess

best best. *See also* **be(n)**

beste (*noun*) beast, animal

284

beth *see* be(n)

bete(n) (bette, beten) to beat, scourge, strike

beye(n) (boghte, boght) to buy, pay for, redeem

bidde(n) (bad, bidde) to ask, bid; command, direct; offer

bifore, biforn before

bihete(n) / bihighte(n) (bihete, bihoten) to promise

biknowe(n) to acknowledge, recognize

bille letter, note

biseche(n) (bisoghte, bisoght) to beseech, implore

bithenke(n) (bithoghte, bithoght) to reflect, bethink, consider; concern (oneself)

bitide(n) to happen, befall

blan *see* blynne

blisse happiness, bliss, joy

blithe happy, glad, blithe

blive quickly, at once

    as / also blive immediately, as quickly as possible

blynne(n) (*pret. s.* blan) to cease (from), stop

bon bone

boon boon, request

boot remedy, redress

bour chamber, bower; dwelling place

brak *see* breke(n)

brast *see* breste(n)

breed bread

breke(n) (brak, breken, broken) to break

brenne(n) (*pret.* brente) to burn

breste(n) (*pret. s.* brast) to burst, break

brigge bridge

burde maiden

bynde(n) (band, bounde, bounden) to bind

cam *see* come(n)

can (*pres. pl.* conne, *pret.* coude / couthe) to know, understand; be able, know how to, can

carpe(n) to converse, speak

cas circumstance, case; affairs; condition, plight

certes certainly, indeed, truly

chaunce chance; event; adventure

chere face, appearance, demeanor; (good) cheer

chese(n) to choose

child child; young person, youth

clene pure; splendid; (*adv.*) entirely

clepe(n) to call; summon; mention

come(n) (cam, comen, comen) to come

coom coming, arrival

corage heart; mind; disposition

cors body, corpse

coude, couthe *see* can

dar (*inf.* durren, *pret.* durste) to dare

dede deed, event, act

deed (*adj., inflected* dede, *and nominal*) *pl.* dede dead

deel part, share, bit, portion

    ilke deel, everich (a) deel all, every part; altogether

deeth death

dele(n) to deal, allot, distribute; deal with

deme(n) to judge, adjudge, deem

dere (*noun*) harm, injury; (*adj.*) dear, beloved, valued; (*adv.*) dearly, at great cost

deye(n) to die

dide *see* do(n)

dighte(n) to prepare, make ready; arrange; array (for battle)

disese discomfort, misery, sorrow

do(n) to do; cause; act; make; put. *Also* **dide** *as preterit auxiliary form*

dol grief, misery; lamentation

doom judgment, decision

doute fear

dradde *see* **drede(n)**

drawe(n) (**drough, drowe, drawen**) to draw, pull; bring

drede fear

drede(n) (**dradde, dred**) to fear

drough, drowe *see* **drawe(n)**

durste *see* **dar**

ech each

    ech a every

echoon each one, every one

eet *see* **ete(n)**

eft again; afterward; thereupon

eke also, moreover

er *comp.* **erre** before, earlier, formerly. *Also* **er-than, er-that**

ere ear

ese ease, comfort; delight, pleasure

ete(n) (**eet, eten**) to eat

everich (**a**) every

everichoon everyone

eye *pl.* **eyen** eye

falle(n) (**fel, felle, fallen**) to fall; befall

fame fame, reputation; report

fare(n) (**ferde, faren**) to go, fare; behave, conduct

faught *see* **fighte(n)**

faute fault

fayn glad; eager, willing. *Also adverb*

feeld (*inflected* **felde**) field

feend *pl.* **fendes** devil; foe

fele many

fele(n) to feel

fell deadly, fierce, cruel

fer *comp.* **ferre** far

ferde *see* **fare(n)**

feyne (**n**) to feign, pretend

fighte(n) (**faught, foghte, foughte**) to fight

flour flower

fond *see* **fynde(n)**

fonde(n) to try, seek, endeavor, test

for- *an intensive prefix, as in* **fordryve(n)** to drive about, **forfaren** to have gone to destruction, **forsmyte(n)** to strike (to death)

forlorn (*p.p. and adj.*) lost; ruined, degraded

for-thy therefore; because

foryete(n) (**foryat, foryeten**) to forget

fowel bird, fowl

free noble, gracious, generous; free

fro from, fro

fynde(n) (**fond, founden**) to find

fyr fire

game, gamen amusement; game, sport; merriment, joy, pleasure

gan (*pret. of* **gynne**) began, undertook (and carried out). *Also a common verb auxiliary indicating past time*: did

gest guest

gete(n) (**gat, geten**) to get, obtain; beget

gilt guilt

glee mirth, pleasure; entertainment; music

go(n) (*Pres. s. 1* go, *2* gost, *3* goth; *pl.* gon; *pres. subj. s.* go, *pl.* gon. *Pret.* went (*see also* **wenden**). *Imp. s.* go, *pl.* goth) to go, walk, move

gost spirit

286

grete(n) (grette, gret) to greet

greve(n) to grieve, aggrieve; harm, injure; offend

halp *see* helpe(n)

hap chance, (good) fortune

hastow = hast thou

have(n) (*Pres. s. 1* have, *2* hast, *3* hath; *pl.* haven; *pres. subj. s.* have, *pl.* haven. *Pret. s. 1, 3* hadde, *2* haddest, *pl.* hadden; *pret. subj. s.* hadde, *pl.* hadden. *P.P.* had. *Imp. s.* have, *pl.* haveth) to have, possess, keep, get

havene harbor

heed head

heer / here here; *pl.* heres hair

heighe high. *See also* hight

hele health; prosperity

hele(n) to heal, restore

helpe(n) (halp, holpen) to help

hende (*adj. and noun*) gracious, courteous, gentle, pleasant (one, person)

heng *see* honge(n)

hennes hence

hente(n) to seize, obtain, get

herber harbor; lodging, shelter

herbere(n) to harbor, protect

here(n) (herde, herd) to hear, listen to. *See also* heer

herte heart; mind

hevy heavy; sad

hewe hue, complexion, appearance

hight high; height

on hight on high, above

hol whole, sound, complete, restored

hoolly (*adv.*) wholly, completely

hom home

hom(e) to home, homeward

hond hand

honge(n) (*pret. s.* heng) to hang

hope(n) to hope; expect, think, suppose

hy haste; *usually in phrase* in hye quickly, in haste, swiftly

hye(n) to hasten

ilke each, every; that ilke that same, that very (one)

kene bold, eager, keen; sharp; cruel

kepe(n) to keep, preserve, take care of; greet

kyn, kynne kin, race, kind

kynde (*noun*) nature; (*adj.*) kind; natural

ladde(n) *see* lede(n)

lasse / lesse less

lat *see* lete(n)

lede(n) (ledde, ladde(n), led / lad) to lead, guide; direct; bring

leef (*noun*) *pl.* leves leaf; (*adj. and nominal*) *inflected* leve dear, beloved; agreeable, desirable; *comp.* levere rather; levere were me I would rather

lemman beloved (one); lover, sweetheart

lenger (*comp. of* longe) longer

lere(n) to teach; learn

lese(n) (*p.p.* lost / lorn) to lose

lete(n) (lett, letten) to let, allow, permit; leave, let go, abandon, forsake. *Also* lat *as verb auxiliary indicating hortative mood*

leve *see* leef

levere *see* leef

leve(n) (lefte, left) to leave; leave off; neglect, abandon

lighten(n) to alight

like(n) to please. *Commonly in impersonal construction: e.g.,* him

287

liketh it pleases him, suits him

lime limb, member

liste(n) *as impersonal verb,* to desire, wish; be pleased: *e.g.,* **me listeth** it pleases me, I desire

lite, litel little, small

lore teaching, instruction

lorn *see* **lese(n)**

loude loud. *Also adverb*

lufsom lovesome; beautiful, lovely

lust pleasure, desire, delight; lust

lusty desirable, pleasant

mad *see* **make(n)**

madd mad

make mate; match

make(n) (**made, mad**) to make; do; cause

man (*noun*) man, person; (*indefinite pronoun*) one, anyone, someone

mankynde, mankynne mankind

may (*noun*) maiden; *pres. pl.* **mowe,** *pret.* **myghte** may, can, be able, be permitted

mayn might, strength

  at his mayn with his utmost ability

  of mayn strong

mede reward, compensation, meed

mele meal, repast

mete food

meynee body of servants or retainers, household attendants; company

mo more

moder mother

mone lamentation, complaint; moon

mood mood, spirit, temper; thought; mind

moot (*pres. s.* 1, 3 **moot,** 2 **most,** *pl.* **mote;** *pret.* **moste**) must; can; may

moste (*adv.*) most, mostly, for the most part. *See also* **moot**

morwe morning, morrow; day

mote *see* **moot**

mowe *see* **may**

muche, muchel much; great, large. *Also adverb*

murne(n) to mourn, lament, sorrow, grieve

myddel middle; waist

myght might, power

  at his myght to the utmost of his strength (or ability)

myrie (**murier, muriest**) merry, gay, joyous, pleasant. *Also adverb*

myrthe joy, mirth; amusement; pleasure

myschief misfortune, distress, adversity, trouble

mysese discomfort; trouble, harm

myslike(n) to displease. *As impersonal verb:* to be displeased, made unhappy

nam *see* **nyme(n)**

namore = **no more**

ne *a negative grammatical particle*

nede, nedes (*adv.*) of necessity, necessarily

neer *see* **nere**

neighe(n) to approach, near

nemne(n) to name, mention

nere, nigh (*comp.* **neer**) near

nis = **ne is**

niste = **ne wiste**

noght (*noun*) nothing (at all); (*adv.*) not, not at all

no-kyn no kind (of), none

nolde = **ne wolde**

nome(n) *see* **nyme(n)**

nother neither

nyl = **ne wyl**

nyme(n) (**nam, nomen, nomen**) to
take, seize, catch, go (one's way)

of of; off; from
oght aught, ought, anything; (*adv.*)
at all
oghte *see* owe(n)
one, oone (*adv.*) alone, only. *See
also* **oon**
ones once
oon (*pronoun*) one (person, thing,
etc.); (*adj.*) one, a single
at one in agreement
ore favor; grace, mercy
oth oath
other (*inflected* **othre**) (*adj.*) second, other; (*nominal*) other,
others; (*conj.*) or; either
owe(n) (*pret.* **oghte**) to have, have
to, be obligated, ought
owene own

parfay (*interjection*) by my troth,
faith
payde, payed pleased, satisfied
peyne pain, distress, suffering
peyne(n) to cause pain; to take
pains, endeavor
pere equal, peer
pleye(n) to play, amuse oneself
pleying play, amusement, sport, entertainment
poure poor
preye(n) to pray; ask; beseech
prike(n) to prick, spur, urge;
gallop
pris worth, excellence, value; prize
bere the pris be the most distinguished, worthy
of pris excellent, precious
prively privately, secretly, inti-
mately
privetee privacy, secrecy, secret
matter or thing

privy private, secret, hidden
pyne torment, pain, misery

quelle(n) to kill

rathe, rathely quickly; soon
rede advice, counsel; plan, strategy
rede(n) (*pret. s.* **radde**) to advise,
counsel; plan; read
reherce(n) to repeat, recount
renne(n) (**ran, ronne, ronne**) to
run; go; flow
reve(n) (*pret.* **refte**) to take away,
bereave, deprive; rob, steal
rewe(n) to pity; rue, regret. *Also in
impersonal construction: e.g.,* (it)
reweth me, me reweth I regret,
pity
right (*noun*) right, rights, justice;
(*adj.*) right, true; (*adv.*) straight,
right, directly, exactly, just
wyth righte rightfully
rise(n) (**ros, rise, risen**) to rise,
arise
rode rood, cross
ronne *see* renne(n)
ros *see* rise(n)
route host, company, rout, (great)
number
routhe pity, compassion; pitiful
sight or thing

same, samen together
al samen all together, with one
accord
sauf safe
seche(n) (**soghte, soght**) to seek,
search
see(n) (**saw** = **seigh, sawe, seen** /
sene) to see, perceive
seemly seemly, fair, lovely, becom-
ing
seigh(e) *see* see(n)

seint saint

semblaunt semblance, appearance, looks; countenance

sene visible, manifest. *See also* **see(n)**

sete *see* **sitte(n)**

seye(n), seyn (seyde, seyd) to say; tell; speak

shal (*pres. pl.* **shullen,** *pret.* **sholde**) shall, will; am to (is to, *etc.*); ought to. *Also as auxiliary verb*

shaltow = shalt thou

shape(n) (shoop, shope, shapen) to make, devise; ordain, appoint; intend; prepare

sheeld (*inflected* **shelde**) shield

shende(n) to destroy, ruin. *P.P. and adj.* **shent** ruined, destroyed, brought to nothing

shilde(n) to shield, protect

sholde *see* **shal**

shrynke(n) to shrink, wither

shulle *see* **shal**

sighte *see* **sike(n)**

sik (*noun*) sigh; (*adj.*) sick

sike(n) (*pret.* **sighte**) to sigh; regret

siker (*adj.*) sure, certain, secure; **sikerly** (*adv.*) certainly

siknesse sickness

sith (*adv. and conj.*) after, afterward; since, after; when **sithen** after, afterward

sithe, sithes times

sitte(n) (sat, sete, seten) to sit

slee(n) / **slo (slough, slowe, slayn** / **slawen)** to strike; slay

slepe(n) (*pret. s.* **sleep,** *pl.* **slepe**) to sleep

smertly quickly, promptly; sharply, curtly

smot *see* **smyte(n)**

smyte(n) (smot, smyte, smyten) to smite, strike

so so; as

socour help, succor

socoure(n) to help, succor

soghte *see* **seche(n)**

solace(n) to delight; console

solas delight; consolation; amusement, pleasure, entertainment; comfort

somdel somewhat

somer springtime

som-tyme once (formerly); sometimes

sone son

song song. *See also* **synge(n)**

sonne sun

sooth (*inflected* **sothe**) (*noun*) (the) truth; (*adj.*) true
  for sothe forsooth, in truth, truly

sore (*noun*) pain, sore, misery; (*adj.*) sore, grievous, painful; (*adv.*) sorely, grievously, painfully; exceedingly

sorwe sorrow, grief, pain

sorwe(n) to sorrow, grieve

sothe *see* **sooth**

spede(n) to succeed, prosper; fare

speke(n) (spak, speke, spoken) to speak

spere spear

spor spur

sprynge(n) to spring; sprout, grow

stark strong, powerful

stede (1) place; (2) steed

sterte(n) (*pret. s.* **stirte**) to start up (out, *etc.*); leap, spring

stille (*adj.*) still, quiet; (*adv.*) ever, always; quietly, silently, motionlessly

stonde(n) (*pret. s.* **stood,** *pl.* **stode**) to stand

stounde space of time; short interval

stour (*noun*) (armed) combat; (*adj.*) strong, stalwart stout strong; proud; stately

stynte(n) to stint; cease, stop

styrop stirrup

swerd sword

swete sweet, fair, pleasant. *Also as nominal:* sweet (one), *etc.*

swithe very (much), exceedingly; quickly

synge(n) (song, songen) to sing

synne sin

take(n) (took, toke, taken / tane) to catch, take, seize; entrust

tane *see* take(n)

telle(n) to tell, recount; enumerate, count

tente intent; notice, heed

tere (*noun*) tear

than then, thereupon; afterward; consequently

thanne than

that (*demonstrative pronoun*) *pl.* tho that, those; (*relative pronoun*) that

thenke(n) (thoghte, thoght) to think, conceive, consider

thennes thence

ther there; there (the place) where

thilke = the ilke

this *pl.* thise this, these

tho then, (*rarely*) when. *See also* that

thoghte *see* thenke(n) and thynke(n)

thole(n) to suffer, endure

throwe space of time, interval

thurgh through, by means of, because of

thyng *pl.* thyng / thynges thing; *pl.* things, affairs, matters

thynke(n) (thoghte, thoght) (*impersonal verb*) to seem (to)

tide (1) time, occasion; (2) tide (of the sea)

tite quickly, immediately

to- *an intensive prefix, as in* to-blowe(n) to blow about violently, to-breke(n) to break in pieces, to-ryve(n) to tear apart, split apart

to (*prep.*) to; (*adv.*) too

togidre together

trewe true

trouthe troth, truth

trowe(n) to believe, think

uncouth strange, foreign; unknown

under under, beneath; behind

unethe, unethes scarcely, with difficulty

wan pale, wan; dark. *See also* wynne(n)

war cautious, wary; observant; discreet. *Commonly in phrase* war and wys, *a formula of general approbation and respect*

waxe(n) (wex, wexen, waxen) to wax, grow; become

wede (*often in plural* wedes) garment(s), clothing, attire (including armor)

weder weather

wel well; many, much; easily; good; very

welde(n) to wield; control; rule, command

wele happiness, good fortune; wealth, prosperity

wende(n) (*pret.* wente) to turn, change; go (away), depart. *See also* wene(n)

wene(n) (*pret.* wende) to expect; suppose, imagine; think

wepe(n) to weep

werke(n) (wroghte, wroght) to work, cause, make, bring about

weylawey (*interjection*)

whan when

whil (*conj.*) while

while (*noun*) a time, a while

whilom formerly, once

wide wide, broad; (*adv.*) widely, far and wide

wight (*noun*) person, wight, creature; (*adj.*) valiant, swift, nimble; (*adv.*) quickly, straightway

wighte weight

wisse(n) to guide, direct, instruct

wite(n) (*pres. s. 1, 3* wot, *2* wost; *pl.* wite; *pret.* wiste) to know, learn, be aware, be assured

wo woe

wode wood, woodland, forest. *See also* wood

wol *see* wylle

wone(n) to dwell, remain, live

wonne *see* wynne(n)

wood (*inflected* wode) mad

wot *see* wite(n)

wreke(n) (wrak, wreken / wroken) to revenge; wreak (vengeance)

wroght(e) *see* werke(n)

wrong (*noun*) wrong, injustice; (*adj.*) wrong, unjust

  wyth wronge wrongfully

wronge wrongfully, unjustly

wroth angry, wroth

wyl, wylle will, desire; purpose, intention

wylle (*Pres. s. 1, 3* wyl, wol, *2* wylt, wolt; *pl.* wol, wolle. *Pret. s.* wolde, *pl.* wolden) to wish, will, desire, be willing. *Also as auxiliary verb*

wynne joy, bliss

wynne(n) (wan, wonne) to win, get, gain; make one's way

wys wise. *See also* war

wyse manner, wise, way, fashion

yaf *see* yeve(n)

yave *see* yeve(n)

yate gate

yede (*a preterit form*, often in suppletion with go(n)) walked, fared, went

yeer *pl.* yeres year; yere *commonly after a numeral*

yerne eagerly, gladly, quickly

yelde(n) (*pret.* yolde) to yield, submit; repay

yeve(n) (yaf, yave, yeven) to give, grant

y-fere together

yift gift

yolde *see* yelde(n)

yore a long time (ago), of old

yvel evil, wicked; difficult

yvele evilly, wickedly; unfortunately, unhappily, ill

y-wis certainly, indeed, truly